WITH A PINCH OF SIN

With a Pinch of Sin

HARRY J. BOYLE

PaperJacks

A division of General Publishing Co. Limited
Don Mills, Ontario

The discipline of writing a weekly column for the
Saturday editorial page of the Toronto *Telegram*
and the good nature of the editors have simplified
the construction of *With a Pinch of Sin* and made it
possible.

Harry J. Boyle

Published in PaperJacks 1973
Reprinted by arrangement with
Doubleday Canada Limited.

ISBN 0-7737-7032-1
Printed and bound in Canada

For W. A. B.

CONTENTS

CHAPTER 1

GOD AND THE METHODISTS

It may have been the "Roaring Twenties," but to me, growing up on an Ontario farm tucked away in a valley near Lake Huron, it was a time of peace, dominated more or less by God and the Methodists!

First of all there was God. Father Morrison kept impressing us about the Divine Presence in our weekly catechism lessons to the point where you could look up in the sky and sense that you were being constantly watched. I was perplexed over the heavenly system of checks and balances in bookkeeping my faults and scanty virtues. There was further confusion in contrasting the habit of my mother in offering up trials and tribulations to "Our Blessed Lord," while it seemed that Father and Grandfather naturally reserved a good deal of their awe of the divinity for Sundays.

Then there were the Methodists!

We had the white-brick Methodists on our concession in Clover township. The red-brick Methodists, or what the township people called the "shouters" held forth in Clover, our nearest village. Now, if God didn't have time to pay much attention to the hamlet during the week, it was a cinch God couldn't overlook it on a Sunday when all our churches assaulted the heavens with full fervor. In summertime they might be joined by a revivalist tent meeting. In winter the revivalists used a sample room in the Commercial Hotel or the Oddfellows Hall.

On the concession, things were a little quieter. We were divided about half Catholic and half Methodist, with an occasional Anglican, and a Welsh family who bemoaned the lack of what they called "chapel." They finally joined the Baptists in the village.

We went to Mass every Sunday morning, as well as on such holy days as Christmas and New Year. An earlier priest had Devotions with Benediction on Sunday evenings, but Father Morrison compromised by saying Benediction after Mass on Sunday mornings. There were also Stations of the Cross during Lent on Friday afternoons, which were compulsory for students at the separate school.

The Scotch were in the next township of Maple and were divided into Presbyterians, who had an organ in the church, and ones where a precentor led the hymns and took his pitch from a tuning fork. Church Union was a constant subject in those days which Catholics kept away from even mentioning. The Methodists had an afternoon service and an evening service. They had good turnouts in the morning but admitted that the Sunday evening service attracted the more devout as well as young people with perhaps a greater interest in the opposite sex than in the service. The older people lamented in time, the inroads made on the evening attendance by the radio lineups of such programs as Joe Penner, Jack Benny, and Charlie McCarthy. Catholics simply hoped that Father Morrison enjoyed radio as much as they did.

My religious training began with prayers. It was a matter of tradition and pride that each child must learn prayers of a simple nature before attending school and even before learning to read. At school there was a morning period devoted to catechism, in preparation for the Friday visits of our parish priest, Father Morrison.

I can still feel the dreadful apprehension of waiting at school while the middle-aged man with the thinning ruff of sandy hair and a peppering of tobacco ashes erupting from the furrows of his vest walked slowly to the front of the classroom. He turned, adjusted his glasses, and pulled from his pocket a tattered and dog-eared copy of the Catechism, which he didn't consult but used as a pointer. Then he moved to our side of the room where the beginners sat in small, battle-scarred desks.

"We'll start with the little tads," he said with a grin that eased the situation slightly.

It was momentary, because he turned solemn in asking, "Who made the world?"

Five hands with fingers snapping shot aloft.

"I can see . . . I can see," he said, pointing the Catechism at me.

Unwinding myself and sending my slate pencil clattering to the floor I said breathlessly, "God."

Then I sat down with as much sense of accomplishment as if I had just passed a bar examination. Thus was begun a religious education that was to be intertwined through grade school, touched on sketchily during continuation, and would come back with full force at college.

As a youngster I didn't associate religion with my playmates of Methodist parents, but I was soon to learn that they had their discipline as well. On Sunday mornings they took their places in the basement of the white-brick church for Sunday school. It seemed from hearsay to bear a strong resemblance to what we received in catechism classes. On this we could find agreement, especially in regard to creation.

When it came time for First Communion and the preparatory Confession, the differences became apparent. In a way, after several exploratory conversations we avoided it, because we were growing up in a time and place of comparative tolerance. Ancestors, in this valley which had been settled early by pioneers, had nourished prejudices cradled in the religious differences of the Old Country. Most of them had passed away or were muted by old age and experience. They were probably latent in some of my relatives, but apart from reiteration of the necessity to "Keep the Faith," displayed on a sampler in our front hallway, they learned to live and let live. It is significant that the sampler had been moved by my mother from the kitchen to the front hallway where it was seldom seen by anyone outside of our family.

St. Peter's Catholic Church on the concession had been built by local men with more knowledge of barn framing than church construction. The boxiness was relieved by the finger of spire and cross, which pointed heavenward. Inside there was a choir loft with a wheezy organ at the back, reached by an almost perpendicular stairway. Boys going to the choir were expected to look at the steps if they followed girls up the steep stairs.

The pews were boxy and the floor was covered by highly varnished brown linoleum. The walls were pierced by stained-glass windows donated by parishioners in memory of departed relatives. The somber walls were relieved by framed lithographed pictures depicting the Stations of the Cross. The communion rail from which hung a white communion cloth, kept clean and highly starched by members of the Altar Society, separated the sanctuary from the church proper. There was a high altar and two replicas on the side. A sanctuary lamp burned continuously.

With flowers as decorations except during Lent and Advent, the church was somewhat colorful. I had often wondered about the interior of the Methodist church, and one day in passing found the door open. It was being repainted and the painters had evidently gone to the river to have their lunch.

In fear and trepidation I slipped in and looked around. It was varnished and clean and most austere with rows of pews, a pulpit, and an organ at the front of the church. There was a single decoration hanging behind the pulpit which proclaimed, "I AM THE RESURRECTION AND THE LIFE," in simple black letters on a white background.

I sat down in a pew and looked around and then, fancying I heard a sound, left hurriedly. All the way down the road I tried to reconcile it with our own church, settling in a very simple way that we had at least one thing in common. We both had uncomfortable pews.

In our community we were caught on the twin horns of Methodist and Catholic applications of morality. They were often startlingly similar. There was a common accord about most of the things which could be called sinful. There was little or no disagreement about the deadly sins. Where the two churches parted company, however, was on the simple matter of Sunday.

The Catholics looked on the Lord's Day in a much more liberal way than the Methodists. The Methodists were inclined to make it a day of solemnity, and most of them would not purchase anything on Sunday.

One of the principal forms of enjoyment for the Catholics, however, was to congregate in the general store operated by my uncle immediately after Mass. They chatted and talked and did some shopping. Most of them had bought everything needed on Saturday, but they always managed to think up something for Sunday purchase.

The pattern never varied. Just before Mass had finished formally, my uncle, looking as if God or nature had called

him, picked up his hat, made a hasty genuflection, and tip-
toed out on squeaky shoes across the varnished, open space
at the back of the church.

This had been a pew section, but it was removed when
it developed into a haunt for bachelors, widowers, husbands
with pregnant wives, and youngsters without strong pa-
rental control. With a dip at the holy-water font, Uncle
would pry open the big double doors and make a dash for
the store across the road.

On Sundays the front doors of the store were never
opened. A side door was used, and the blinds remained
drawn. The crowd of men, women, and children packed
into the darkened store. It gave the feeling of an illicit
meeting.

At the time I didn't think much about it. There was fun
in being asked to help out with the clerking. The place was
crowded and friendly. There was also a good deal of kidding
and joshing.

"You're sure you gave me the proper weight there?"

I indignantly replied I had, and everyone laughed. Conversation was brisk at first. People pretended they were in
a hurry to have their orders filled. They wanted bread and
staples such as sugar and oatmeal and perhaps bacon as a
Sunday treat. Regular items were chewing or smoking
tobacco.

The only time my uncle might be provoked was when
someone asked for kerosene or machine oil or axle grease.
He felt quite rightly these were items which could have
been bought at another time.

The orders were filled, and still the people waited and
talked. Finally a woman would tug at her husband's coat
sleeve or even make a point of leaving to go out to the car
or the horse and buggy. In winter, most of them huddled
over the big heater and made a ceremony out of pulling on

their gloves or mittens and buttoning up coats. Most of the men would move away.

There were always a few stragglers left. They stood around shredding away at bits and pieces of conversation. "Well we must be going and let you folks get your dinner."

My aunt went to the kitchen, and my uncle made a noisy ceremony of taking down the big, flat racks of the old-fashioned bookkeeping system to mark in the purchases from the notes he had in a small counter book or on a pad. People seemed reluctant to pay cash on the Lord's Day.

When the store was finally deserted, I waited anxiously to see if I was going to be allowed to stay on for dinner. It usually worked, because my uncle and aunt were childless and they enjoyed having company on Sunday. To be allowed to walk around the store in the half-light from the shuttered windows and look at all the stock at close hand was an experience to delight any boy.

Here on the one side were the big bins and the barrels with staples in them. The bins were dark-stained with fierce black lettering on the front. The barrels swung out from under the counter on casters, and contained brown sugar, white sugar, oatmeal, and raisins. Other smaller ones had prunes and apricots and currants and still others had smaller compartments with spices in them.

A large, square glass case displayed candies and chocolate bars and ring sticks and licorice whips and pipes and bull's eye candies. I could also busy myself in lining up the packages of cigarettes and the chewing and smoking tobacco.

I liked setting the tins in line on the shelves. Here were products from faraway places! Salmon from British Columbia, sardines from Nova Scotia and Norway. Raisins in flat, open boxes from Australia, figs packed in bags from Smyrna.

The oranges were in pink wrappers proclaiming that they were Sun-kist in California.

There was a square glass case with a ferocious-looking knife on a wheel poised over a big round of cheese. Cheese to this day has never tasted as good as the occasional slice whittled from that round.

In the wintertime there was a barrel of salt herring sitting between the front door of the store and the storm door. It was there for Lenten demand. Salt herrings freshened out and cooked with potatoes and onions was a treat you could expect once or twice in the winter season.

I liked to look at the collection of patent medicines. There was a great variety of painkillers. There was also a profusion of salves and ointments and pills for backaches and internal disorders. I was much older before I learned at a township dance that the patent medicines, because of their high alcoholic content, were in great demand as a stimulant during the time of the Canada Temperance Act.

One counter held nothing but overalls, smocks, and work shirts and rough sweaters with big collars. I desperately wanted a red and white mackinaw and red peaked cap, but somehow never managed to get them.

In the storeroom there was a collection of everything from flour and feed to plowshares and harness and tangled rolls of barbed wire.

Then my aunt would call me for dinner. That was a treat, because she always had something different, such as small, crispy gherkins or "boughten" chili sauce to go along with fresh boiled ham, and, to finish, a dessert to please the sweet tooth of a curious boy. She never once said, "You'll ruin your teeth!"

My uncle moved to a couch for a rest while my aunt gathered up the dishes, and I knew it was time to go. Then she gave me the comic papers saved from packing cases in the store, and I set out for home.

On the way I met Henry Higgins, and he and I looked for someplace to spend an hour poring over the papers and catching up on Mutt and Jeff and Barney Google, but we had to do it quietly, because his father was very strict about Sunday and allowed only religious reading on that day. I felt a little guilty, until I asked my grandfather about it.

He smiled and said, "Don't worry too much. Take when your mother is making a stew. She puts a pinch of spice in it. That's what makes it good. Well, boy, life is a kind of stew, and no matter what anybody says it goes better with a pinch of sin. Not too much, mind you. Just a pinch."

He winked then and added, "But I'd keep that to myself."

I did, and it was a wonderfully comforting philosophy to combat the pangs of an easily stimulated conscience.

CHAPTER 2
SEPARATE SCHOOLS

While I must say that Catholics and Methodists lived in harmony for the most part, it would be unfair to say that there were no signs of rivalry between the children. It largely came about because we were attending separate schools. You were a constant companion to the children on the next farm up until you reached the minimum age for school, and then suddenly you were divided, without ever getting a really satisfactory reason for the change.

It was difficult to form friendships at school and not have them interfere with the old fellowship. Petty rivalries broke out, and probably the strongest one of all concerned the Kennans and the Keegs. I have a smug sense of satisfaction every time I hear someone praising the chariot race scene of *Ben Hur*. They should have seen the charioteers from our school on the concession, when I was a boy in the country.

Every morning and evening of the school term, this race took place. The basis of it was the rivalry of two sets of cousins.

In normal events of living, cousins often seem to form better relationships and terms than do brothers and sisters or, particularly, brothers and brothers. In this case, that didn't apply. A form of feuding went on between the Kennans and the Keegs. They lived across from each other on the concession. They were cousins.

The Kennans were Methodists and the Keegs were Catholics as a result of a mixed marriage.

Since they lived a considerable distance from school, the children were provided with semiretired mares and somewhat rickety buggies. There were three Kennans and two Keegs. In each case the eldest was a girl. Bena Keeg was tall and gangling. Nada Kennan was a daintier-looking soul with soft, rusty hair that framed a cute but freckled face. They were the charioteers.

Each morning, when chores and breakfast were over, they would come out on the concession. Sometimes one was ahead and sometimes the other. They drove sedately down the road through a small hollow and up over the crest of the hill in front of the old Doyle place, which was a grass farm. Then, as they passed from sight of their respective homes, the race was on.

They raced along their concession and then up the side road to the sixth concession. The corner of the side road and the sixth was the unofficial goal, just by the big beech tree with the crooked limb.

Bena planted her feet against the base of the dashboard, edged her brother back on the seat, let her arms flow out loosely and yelled in a voice to stun a Comanche: "NELL . . . NELL . . . TAIL UP, NELL."

Old Nell would bunch her tired muscles, awkwardly reapportion her somewhat ungraceful self, and take off.

Nada had two young ones for ballast. She sat in the middle, looking prim, but with a wrist-snapping action that told on Old Belle, her charger.

"BELLE . . . BELLE . . . BELLE . . . BELLE . . ."
She shouted it over and over, hypnotizing the elderly roan

to whinny, toss her head, and splay her feet because of her strange gait.

Up to the top of the Lidy hill and then down to the place where the culvert narrowed to one passage . . . Keeg ahead . . . and then Kennan, swinging out over a roadside to gain an advantage and rushing for the narrow culvert.

In the summertime it didn't matter, because one or the other took the slight edge and dashed across the dry creek bed. In spring rushet time, they dared not try it. All the time, the war whoops of the younger fry kept encouraging them.

It became exciting when the girls reached the corner for the turn of the side road. Each had her own technique for preventing an overturn. Nada used her brother and sister for ballast. Bena stood up and planting a foot on each side of the buggy box shifted her weight like a man in a small skiff.

There were some good wide stretches on the side road where they raced neck and neck, but the next hazard was the long swamp. It had one track, oozing muck on each side. They edged on occasion with wheels touching to make that final dash into the swamp.

That they were dangerous no one denied, but no one complained. Well, Mrs. Simpson was once unfortunate enough to be in a democrat with two cases of eggs on the back, coming toward them, and had to take to the soft muck.

The next hazard was a narrow cut in the hill. Only one could go at a time.

When they turned the final corner and came swooping by my uncle's general store, it often caused a real commotion, particularly on the morning of beef ring, when there would be a sizable gathering of horses and rigs.

The last and trickiest maneuver was to make it through the narrow gateway on the way to the shed where the horses were kept.

Just to see Bena Keeg standing up, her long, black hair streaming in the wind and the slack end of the lines lathering across the rump of Old Nell, was something that commercial travelers and other visitors talked about for years.

It was the custom in those days to take turns inviting the schoolteacher for weekends. Miss Loomis, the public school teacher went on a Friday night to the Kennans, and by an agreed armistice they didn't race along the side road and the concession people stared in disbelief.

The following Monday morning, however, as they crested the Doyle hill, the Keeg boy whooped and the automatic reaction came over Bena Keeg, who jumped to action and flailed at Old Nell.

They were off, and Miss Loomis was an unwilling passenger in the Kennan buggy, being buffeted from side to side by the youngsters. All went well until they tried to round the corner near the shed. The Kennan chariot lost a wheel and sent all the passengers into the burdock and goldenrod-infested roadside.

That settled it for some time, although Miss Loomis was a good sport and dismissed school at noon for a reason which still makes former members of the school board chuckle. She called it "seasickness."

There was a good deal of resentment in the separate school. Our only consolation was the fact that on church holy days, after attending Mass we had a holiday, a fact which caused a good deal of resentment amongst the public school students.

All schools, public and separate, coming under the jurisdiction of the Provincial Department of Education competed at the annual township school fair. This was an event of great importance, pooling the Chicago Fair, the Royal Winter Fair, and the Canadian National Exhibition in Toronto.

One year we had an ardent teacher who was not above entering a dash of religious competition into the whole affair. She had been reared in the Catholic devotion of Dublin and I suspect considered her fellow communicants in Clover township as being a bit slack in their religious ardor. She gave an impassioned lecture on the importance of the event with several allusions to the importance of making a good showing as Catholic students.

I was too young and too small to contribute to such things as the tug-of-war, and had no particular aptitude for making milk stools and those awkward bookcases which always caused parents a great deal of embarrassment when they were installed in their front parlors. In the first place there was an acute shortage of books, and in the second place the constructions were always a bit tipsy in their design and execution.

Anyway, I was determined to help Miss Grubb as much as possible. I was loyal.

She stood with a pencil poised over a pad. I had, along with all the other pupils in our one-room school, a copy of the prize list, a flimsy yellow sheet with lists of items.

The school fair board gave us a choice of seeds, some with names we had never heard of before, and we were to plant them in our own plots. With harvesttime we were supposed to have magnificent specimens—the kind of glories pictured in Father's seed catalogue—and display them to the critical judgment of the local experts.

Miss Grubb gave us a few minutes to study the list of seeds. Then she said:

"What will you have?"

My eye caught something, and I blurted out, "Green Mountain Potatoes."

This brought a remark from her about the possibility of my taking Irish Cobblers. I stuck to Green Mountains. She looked a little piqued and asked me what else I was going to take. My eye fell on something called cosmos. She shrugged and put it down. At the time I thought cosmos were vegetables.

I was the butt of a lot of jokes in planting time when the seeds arrived. Cosmos turned out to be flowers. It was unthinkable in that day and age for a boy to ask for flower seeds. That was reserved for girls.

I took home the small white sack of Green Mountains, which interested my father, because they were registered seed. I scattered the cosmos seed.

Father looked at the potatoes and said: "Must put them off by themselves. If they turn out well, it would give us a new seed start."

This heartened me immensely, but then he seemed to lose interest.

My plot was given a complete working over. The soil was reduced to the consistency of dust. I fenced it with a make-shift set of barriers and made up my mind that there wouldn't be a weed allowed. Every morning on the way to school and at night on the way home I watered the plot and carried on weed executions.

At one point Grandfather suggested that I might be discouraging plants as well as weeds, and so I slackened up. The potatoes came along well, and the flowers popped up in profusion. Mother thought it was a splendid idea to have flowers, but Father looked amused.

The potatoes had a little trouble. There was a rule which I later learned no one bothered with, saying that all the work had to be performed by the students. I took this for gospel and wouldn't let Grandfather help me. The result was that the potatoes had been cut strangely and planted awkwardly and had to fight their way up.

When school reconvened in the fall, there was a great fuss over the matter of the fair entries. Girls spent recess time working on lace doilies and caps. Other students boasted about their vegetables or their carpentry prowess.

My faith was shattered a bit when I heard our neighbor Mrs. Higgins complain about being so busy, "putting up preserves for Rose Marie to enter at the school fair."

I complained to my mother that this looked like cheating on behalf of the public school students. My mother shushed me, and at the time I thought she hadn't paid any attention to me. This hurt, but on the night before we were to go to the school fair, I went out and looked at the potatoes and the cosmos, which certainly seemed fragile. I wasn't going to bother entering them, but my mother said I had gone so far and there could be no backing down.

The night before the fair was torment. I couldn't sleep, and at five o'clock in the morning I was trying to impress my parents with the need for promptness.

We paraded to the fair grounds behind a quick-marching pipe band. There were a lot of speeches. The reeve spoke and so did every chairman of every school board. The local member of Parliament was listened to because he put up five dollars in prize money.

Finally we were allowed in the hall. I felt like crying when I saw that my potatoes hadn't even won a consolation prize. The cosmos, however, took second prize, and that cheered me. I resolutely didn't think about the fact that there were only two entries.

I dragged my feet as Mother moved along looking at preserves and handwork and then the art exhibits, and suddenly she nudged me and said: "Look, you have a first prize for penmanship."

It was true. Mother stared in disbelief, because she was always chiding me for being a careless writer. At home my father looked quizzically at the ribbon. I had won one dollar for the penmanship and fifty cents for the cosmos.

My mother horrified me on the following Sunday by saying haughtily to Rose Marie's mother: "Well, my son at least did all the work himself, in connection with his entries at the school fair."

I never did have the heart to tell her that Miss Grubb did . . . well . . . she did kind of help me . . . in a way with my handwriting entry. But, of course, I hadn't even known she was going to enter it. There was no sin in that!

CHAPTER 3

THE VILLAGE

Clover was the focal point for our community, although we did have two churches, two schools, and a general store in our own township. The village, almost a metropolis to my unsophisticated eyes had the railroad depot, a bank, the gristmill and a great many churches.

Country people had a certain feeling about the village.

"It must be an awful place to be stuck in when you retire."

That was the most common remark about the place, and yet every farmer in the township hoped someday to save up enough money to buy a place in the village. Half the seven-hundred-odd residents were already retired farmers from the township.

It was natural for country people to keep a close eye on village activities. The phenomenon of modern living is that so many people work harder than ever to get away from village and rural life. They move to live and work in the almost smothering complexes of very large cities. Then they work even harder to go back to the country or create something in the urban area approximating the village and rural life which they were so anxious to leave.

The village was never perfect. I suppose it was less complicated. A village, like a rural community of any kind, had a sense of interdependence. This, in effect, was a holdover from pioneer days. Man, in a form of contest with nature, couldn't battle it alone.

In Clover you saw the life cycle from birth to death, and the emotions were well represented. They were all there, from jealousy to anger to charity and some humility.

Our village of Clover started, I suppose, in the same way as most hamlets. It happened. Nature helped by placing certain characteristics in a certain place. There was, first of all, a river which was a source of food, transportation, and ultimately power. There was a tract of arable land that was well drained and there was plenty of forest for fuel and lumber.

This was rugged country, and several potential settlers didn't bother to take up their land allotments. One became a bootmaker and another did some woodworking, in time learning to make and repair primitive implements for the pioneers. A British army sergeant with little liking for husbandry turned to being a gunsmith.

Then came a circuit preacher who spouted flaming words about the perdition and damnation afoot, with special reference to rum, whiskey, and gin. He conveniently overlooked the fact that he had been loaned the barroom by an innkeeper with a sense of quizzical tolerance. It wasn't overlooked by the residents of the village, and they built a hall which became a church, and then as the village grew the number of churches grew out of all proportion to the people. It was some time before they felt the need for a school, using a church hall for that purpose.

I suppose our village had a design. This was largely a matter of building houses in such a way that they didn't destroy trees. That's why there was an abrupt jog in Main Street by the smithy. Shade and respect for an enormous elm tree with a crooked branch was more important than a straight street. They liked trees in that village.

Care for the trees was responsible for the little hamlet sparkling in the fall like a jeweled piece. The beeches and maples that strayed all over up and down side streets, around the churches on Main Street and the tall poplars that lined the road to the station were just the thing for a setting.

Around the red-brick Methodist church there were sentinel evergreens of a towering size. Farther down the street a blanket of ivy around the Presbyterian church shimmered into a variety of colors.

The Warley sisters, behind the iron fence of their imposing property with the white frame house, cultivated a profusion of flowers.

The barbershop was a one-story affair with a two-story false front, but the open space between sidewalk and store was a source of pride to the barber, who all summer long cultivated magnificent red geraniums, which he carefully slipped and moved inside for winter blooming.

The milliner specialized in beds of petunias. Jimmy Medd, in the tailor shop, had a collection of ferns. The undertaking parlor and furniture store had an austere look about it, but the building seemed lazy and appeared to be gradually settling into the earth. It was, of course, one of the first buildings in the village and had long, rotted-out mudsills.

The upper deck of the veranda of the hotel had a variety of flowers, plants, and shrubs in pots and tubs. The lower veranda was decorated by large chairs and benches occupied all summer long by older men who sat and smoked and gossiped.

While there was a certain rivalry in connection with flowers and shrubs, there was a fierce and undeclared competition as far as gardens were concerned. The front window of the bank and post office in the fall had displays of everything from monster cabbages to pumpkins and squash. There was also a variety of vegetables that had grown in weird shapes.

There was a fierce pride about that village. When a promoter came to town and promised to build a planing mill, they were delighted. It took several sessions of the village council, however, to reach a decision when he wanted a road cut through a treed property set aside for a park. He asked for a direct roadway to the railroad station. The trees were very large and very old, and legend had it that the Indians regarded the grove with some special significance. Some of the younger businessmen were eager to cut down the trees. The older men didn't want it.

The planing-mill man grew disgusted and took his project to a rival village. The argument raged on.

"How can you build a prosperous and modern community with that kind of thinking?" was the cry of the younger men, led by the shoe-store man, who was a newcomer.

"There are some things more important than that kind of progress," said the older men. "Besides, he could have built the mill on the other side of the railroad station."

It was a source of comfort to the veranda group of the Commercial Hotel when the planing-mill man went broke. It was considered a strong form of approval for their decision, and, in spite of modern travel and automobiles, those trees are still there. So is the old elm. They straightened the street, but they saved the tree. It makes me rather proud of Clover.

In the township of Clover and the village of Clover the miller was a man of stature. He was essential, using the water power to convert the wheat from the first plots into flour and the grain into feed. It was part of a natural cycle.

The mill was a fat structure, constructed for the needs of the place and to fit the topography of the riverbank and the location of the race that powered the big wheel. The front side was shorter, and you drove in directly from the roadway. The other side, which overhung the water, was deep and stood like a timbered fortification.

The willows clustered around it like monstrous hens with green feathers. There was also a great old elm that looked as if it had staggered suicidally to the edge of the river, and then in a moment of regret had stopped to permanently clutch, with clawing and exposed roots, for support from falling.

There was a dam which stored up the water for reserve power, channeling it into a race. The water from the race was controlled, spilling into the wooden pockets of the great wheel that clacked and rumbled from the overshoot. The water in the black-green pond behind the dam was calm and freckled in fall by the stray leaves, or else silvered by the reflection of the tall birches that left silver poles on the steady surface. Depending on the season, there was an overflow that knifed in sheets over the edge of the dam, fanned down, and then splashed on the great rocks that had been used for footing.

The mill and the millstream served for many poets as an inspiration. That was natural. The whole place reeked of calm. It was the kind of serenity that comes when man is in tune with nature. The miller harnessed the water, but he didn't destroy or deprive by doing it. The pond came into being, and the willows and the reeds grew and afforded shelter to birds and animals. In the fall the geese and the ducks landed on the surface of the water, and there was an unwritten law that there was to be no interference with the visitors.

On the other hand, it was perfectly acceptable to fish off the dam. Since the miller fed the fish and they were quite sophisticated about taking bait, very few people ever managed to catch any of the chub that grew to be enormous.

The mill smelled inside of flour dust, must, and mouse. The cumbersome wheel outside moved to turn with its shaft an arrangement of sprockets and gears that turned the top stone against the lower stationary one. At first even the gears and sprockets were wooden and homemade, but they were replaced by forged ones.

The miller was a busy man, but moved with a steady dignity. He placed the grain in what was called a shoe that fitted on the grinding stone on top. The grain was forced out through grooves. From time to time the top stone would have to be removed to allow him to sharpen up the grooves. This was a job for a man of skill.

For children a trip to the mill was a delight. A parent was seldom in a hurry when he went for grist. Chances were he would have to leave it and come back another day; but most men unloaded the grain, tethered their horses, and gossiped.

On fall days, with the sun streaming in the open door, this was a place for slow talk and smoking. It was a chance for youngsters to roam through the mill or peer down at the dark water through the trapdoor, where the miller took mysterious soundings, as if he were sailing a ship.

He would stop to make symbols on a board or a shingle because his commission was still roughly reckoned on the same basis as the one established by the first Parliament in Ontario. He was, according to that early statute, entitled to one twelfth of the grain he ground.

Our little mill became less of a community effort and more of a modern enterprise. The new miller started making flour, bran, shorts, and middlings. Farmers grumbled that the miller was more anxious to make and sell flour and by-products than he was to grind their grist. Then the bake-wagons started threading the concessions and side roads and women started buying bread and men started complaining about the quality of the bread served on their tables.

In time the farmers stopped hauling their grain to be ground for grist. The portable mill came on a truck and stopped long enough to grind enough grist for a season. When a housewife baked a batch of bread, it was a noteworthy event or even a reward.

Our mill was moved uptown to a new building where a snorting diesel was installed. The old building degenerated as people stole boards, and wet and weather left it a place of beams, joists, and rafters looking like a decayed prehistoric monster. The dam broke and left chunks like gaping teeth to strain the water of its river, which was now a gentle thing. Somebody sold the trees from the grove and left the bare stumps. The elms and willows looked sadder than ever.

But the whole community, township, and village would get into a ruckus. A real one happened when Clover cast off ties with the township as a mere police village and became a self-governing municipality.

There was an element which said that the ones who didn't have to pay taxes, or the ones who simply didn't pay, such as the Jenks family, were the advocates of the new status of independence.

The gristmill owner and heavy property owners believed they were going to have a bigger share of the tax load to carry. In fact, while the gristmill owner's brother was reeve, it was rumored that the gristmill had been listed on the township rolls as a charitable operation, such as a church.

The man who ran the hide factory was frightened because he had been cheerfully polluting the river with waste for years and was afraid a village council might make him do something about it.

Everyone had an angle!

The Warley sisters were against incorporation. They drove an electric car and refused to pay tax or license fee on it.

Their argument was that the license tax on automobiles was for internal-combustion engines. The constable never got around to getting a ruling on it; the sisters drove it only once a month. Some wag told them that one of the first acts of the new council would be to pass a special license fee on electric cars.

That argument was only a prelude to what happened! Plans were afoot to have a parade on the day of inauguration. There was some talk of making it a three-day reunion.

The reeve and councilors found out, however, that they were caught in the interim between tax collections and they didn't have anything in the till except a small amount from the township and a matching amount from the province.

It was suggested that the clerk write to the premier of the province, inviting him to the celebration and suggesting in a neat way that some form of a special grant would be appreciated. The treasurer said he should write and it was finally decided that the reeve would write and it would be signed double-barreled by the reeve and the treasurer.

The clerk was a bit miffed and suggested that everybody sign it. He further asked what they were going to write on. The village was without stationery.

They told him to go ahead and get some stationery, but he wanted to know what the crest was going to be. The township had a wreath of laurel with a few words in Latin that looked impressive but had actually been taken off a bottle label.

The reeve suggested a photograph of Main Street taken from the east side of the Presbyterian church. This would show the United and Baptist churches, and his feed store, it was quickly pointed out. A photograph of the river flats would show the gristmill and the Jenks shacks, if taken from one angle, and it would show the tannery if taken from the other angle.

The village clerk pointed out that if they were going to be really progressive and inspire confidence in industry to the point of establishing in the village, they had to have class. This meant a symbol of some kind.

They quickly seized on the matter of an industrial symbol, but there wasn't much industry in the village. There was, of course, the sawmill, which was international in the sense that it had once squared ship timbers for England. The tannery wasn't considered to be the proper kind of industry to have represented.

The council sat until two in the morning and couldn't reach a decision. Word of the matter got around next morning by the time Tim Murphy was sweeping the sidewalk in front of his emporium. He had a solution. Have the name Clover superimposed on a shamrock.

This infuriated the harness maker, who suggested during the midmorning refreshment period in the back room of the Commercial Hotel that it should be an orange lily because they grew in superabundance on the river flats. Ed Zinger stopped it short of a religious fist fight.

The next council meeting was a dilly. Everybody was there with a suggestion.

Agatha Simms, who had a deep affection for flying, wanted the crest to have an airplane. Several retired farmers wanted it to be their favorite breed of cattle. Mrs. Henderson, the banker's wife and a city girl who had tried desperately to uplift the community, thought it should be a musical instrument and was indignant when Ed Zinger agreed and said he would plump for a kazoo. The hotel keeper, an ardent foe of the Canada Temperance Act, wanted it to be a sheaf of rye but that suggestion was dropped like a hot potato.

All the ministers in town wanted religious symbols, but they couldn't agree on one.

Father Morrison and Reverend McPherson kept out of the argument. One of the village members suggested a dove with a sprig of clover in its beak. That seemed to take the fancy of the crowd until it was pointed out that a pigeon might be more apt. Most people thought of what the pigeons were doing to the memorial in the square in front of the hall and that was forgotten.

Hjalmar Olsen, the blacksmith, stood up and raised his fist and said, "Yust make it strong. This is strong country. We are strong people." The sight of the muscles of the smithy's arms set the editor of the newspaper to thinking and he said, "By golly I have a clenched fist and strong arm in my typecase that has never been used." People were frazzled out by this time, and they agreed.

That's how Clover came to have the arm, raised fist, and hammer as a crest. It turned out later it was the same one that advertised some kind of washing soda, but people didn't say anything; neither did the township officials, because of their Latin inscription from the medicine bottle, which it turned out concerned internal human disorders.

CHAPTER 4

RELATIVES

Just as physical characteristics of geography and landscape seem to mold people who live and walk in the full exposure of nature, so also do the personal characteristics of his friends and relatives leave an imprint on a child growing up. I'm certain, for instance, that I was influenced by the actions of my parents, grandparents, and close neighbors.

Take the matter of trading. I grew up thinking that my relatives and neighbors must be about the best traders in the world. In fact, I even used to feel sympathetic toward the gypsies who set up on the river flats and proceeded to deal in horses. It seemed a shame for these simple nomads to get involved with the unscrupulous and cagey men of the area.

Gradually, as I grew older, a suspicion formed in my mind that perhaps the big dealers were not as invincible as they liked to suggest.

Higgins, our neighbor, had a rawboned hackney with a fistula that troubled it. He traded it for a stocky coach horse that seemed to be a marvel. The horse had a beautiful coat with two white stockings, and when Higgins drove into town on the following Saturday night he made the full length of the Main Street and then turned back to sta-

ble his horse and rig in the red-brick Methodist church shed.
Just as he made a sweeping turn into the laneway the
horse stopped.

It stopped dead and remained standing there. For two
hours Higgins wheedled, cursed, and cajoled while the Saturday night crowd roasted him unmercifully.

I guess the perfect course of justice was followed when
Grandfather traded the mare with the heaves. Everyone in
the township knew that she had the heaves. On occasion
the mare would start and the neighbors delighted in asking
him if he was driving a mule.

Then he formed an alliance with an Indian who promised, if not to cure the heaves, at least to remove them long
enough for a trade. Grandfather made a trip to Handrich,
the county town, and returned with a sorrel gelding. He was
delighted, having secured ten dollars to boot, in the deal.

Wanting to show off his prowess, he insisted on driving
to church on the following Sunday.

"I tell you lad, there's nothing like dealing. You've got
to have a really sharp eye in your head when you get muck-
ing around with horse traders."

On the way back we took our time. People overtook us
and passed us, and since it was a fine spring day we even
paused to look over the Maitland River bridge at the remains of the spring flood. The water was still dark and
roily.

We got back in the buggy, glorying in the warmth of the
sunshine, and he handed me the reins. I flicked at the sorrel,
and it proceeded to stage a case of heaves that made the
mare look like a beginner.

Grandfather found out later that the Indian specialist
had also worked for the owner of the gelding.

Even my uncle in the general store, who normally stayed
away from trading, fell prey to a trap of another nature. I

was sitting on the front porch of the store and there were several semi-retired farmers smoking and reminiscing.

A Model T touring drove up. A flabby man in a blue suit, wearing a derby and smoking a cigar got out and said, "Who's in charge of the gas pump?" This was a job I welcomed, although in those days the gasoline had to be hand-pumped into a gallon measuring can and then poured by funnel into the tank. It was a fairly tedious job; but I was at the age where self-importance outweighed effort.

The man sat down, mopped his brow, and talked along easily with the loafers. When I finished, he asked me to look at the oil. When the tin hood came up the engine was a dreadful mess. It was covered in a residue of some kind and he roared with laughter, came down and looked at the oil measure and decided he didn't need any. He paid me for the gasoline and ceremoniously gave me a ten-cent tip.

"Is your daddy around?"

I explained that my uncle operated the store.

"Be a good fellow and ask him if he will step out here for a moment or two. I have something very important to show him."

My uncle, dozing on the overall counter, came out sleepily.

"Jonas B. Weatherhead," announced the man.

My uncle nodded.

"Gentlemen, one of the scourges of mankind has been the matter of fire. Fire is the ravenous destroyer that eats up the hard toil of many years and leaves nothing but ashes and sorrow. It kills and maims. For years man has been trying to find a means . . . a safe and effective means of controlling this rapacious destroyer."

He walked around the car dramatically and took a black bag from the back seat. From this he took a round cardboard package with red lettering, which announced that it was a magical fire extinguisher. He opened the top of it, disclosing white powder.

"In the country, where you do not have the benefits of fire companies and fire departments, you are at the mercy of fire."

He paused and pointed dramatically at the group that had shuffled from the front steps and crowded around the car.

"How many times have you seen the world of the work of a fellow farmer destroyed in one night by fire?"

Having allowed them long enough to think about it, he added, "I have the answer to your problems. A great chemist has been working on this problem for many years and he has come up with the solution."

He pointed to the box. "It's there, and I would like to demonstrate it for you. Sir, will you pour some gasoline over the motor of this car?"

My uncle pumped some gasoline into the measure and, walking as if he were hypnotized, poured it on the motor. The man in the derby lit a match and the flames roared up. He pointed at the fire and said, "See the holocaust." Then he reached down and picked up the box and poured a handful of the white powder in his other hand and pelted it with a flinging motion on the engine. The fire was snuffed out.

While the bystanders were still dazed, he rapidly asked them if for only $2.50 they could afford to be without this wonder-working invention. Five of them agreed and the salesman went into a huddle with my uncle. It seems he was not allowed to sell directly to the public.

My uncle was chosen as a dealer and was sold the stuff at wholesale. He was pleased, because there was a liberal profit. The boxes were piled up on the counter and the man departed in his Model T.

Everything would have been all right if the local sawmill

owner hadn't come in before the boxes were sold to the bystanders. He looked at it and grinned.

"I see he took you in too," he said, opening a box, wet-
ting his forefinger, and tasting the powder.

My uncle tasted it as well and his face wrinkled up.

"Soda!"

The boxes were put on a back shelf. My uncle would
never throw them out but kept them as a reminder. Yet, if
he were reminded, he would grow almost apoplectic and
invariably say, "Well, dammit, both the Methodist minister
and the priest bought the stuff from that fellow."

Which really didn't count since there was a general impression that clerics were always soft touches for any kind
of hard salesmanship.

Idleness was something which God, the Methodists, and
even the Catholics, who were often inclined to be more
easygoing, found hard to condone. It was little wonder that
Uncle Denis was a marked man when he came back from
the city. My Uncle Denis, who wasn't really an uncle, but
only seemed like one, quit banking in the city and came
back to live on the farm next to us because he wanted to
think.

This was enough to mark him in a township of hard-
working farmers as being a bit "queer." Relatives shrugged
it off. It would have all passed easily if he hadn't built a
gazebo.

No one in the township had ever heard of a gazebo. I
heard of it when I heard pounding in the orchard on the
way home from school and went to investigate. Uncle
Denis was sawing and hammering, and he had a five-sided
platform affair already laid out.

"Are you building a chicken house?"

He took the excuse to rest and light his pipe.

"No, my boy," he said solemnly, "I am building a gazebo."

"Gazebo . . . gazebo . . . that's fun . . . but what is it?"

Denis was a stocky fellow with sparse hair surmounting a face that wrinkled into laughter very easily. He was then what I thought to be old and now strive to regard as young middle-aged.

"A gazebo, my boy, is a small and useless structure from which a man dedicated to learning may watch the follies of his fellow man and commune with nature."

I went home puzzled but happy that school would soon be over and that I would be able to join my friend in his task.

"Denis is building a gazebo," I announced at suppertime.

My family looked up in bewilderment.

"It must be a colony house," suggested my mother. "That Denis is always codding about things."

Grandfather went over after supper and came back shaking his head.

"He's a bit daft," he said. "He's got a perfectly good veranda if he wants to sit out, but he's making this gazinkus thing for what he calls a place of contemplation."

In the days that followed the gazebo became the main topic of conversation. Denis simply waved at the people who slowed down in passing along the road, but went on with his work. The structure was five-sided, and it had a round roof that went up to a peak like a bell on top of a candy jar. He had latticework on the outside and benches on two sides.

"I can't figure that man out," puzzled Father. "His hay is ready to cut and he's fiddling with that silly house that, as far as I can see, has no useful purpose."

I thought the gazebo was a wonderful idea and tried to

make a call on Denis every night on my way home from school.

"If you pull up that string hanging down in the well, you may get a surprise," he would say. "Bring it along over here."

It was lemonade in a jug, and that was nectar to a small boy on a June day.

There was no mystery to me about the gazebo. It just seemed like a good idea. There was always a trickle of wind through the orchard and you had a wonderful view of the pond, the old farmhouse and the concession road.

"What does he talk about?" inquired my mother when I was late one night for supper.

"Not much," I admitted. "He has lemonade and he tells me about the city and sometimes he reads."

Mother was worried; that was obvious. Later I heard her talking to Father.

"It's not that I don't like Denis," she said. "He's a very nice man. He seems almost like one of the family; but he may be getting strange . . . living alone and all that. He really should be married."

"Oh, I think Denis knows what he's doing," replied Father. "The thing I can't understand is his reputation as such a good businessman. You know, he doesn't seem to care very much about what happens on the farm. He started taking the hay off and then turned around and gave it to Higgins on a very generous share basis. He sits in that silly little shack and reads, while Higgins is taking off the hay. I don't understand that."

The mystery grew like a canker in the community. One Sunday Father Morrison in a half-apologetic way preached about the evils of idleness. We heard that the lean, lanky Reverend McPherson of the white-brick Methodist church had unleashed a hell-raiser about "Mischief and Idle Hands and the Devil."

Grandfather had been over the night before and didn't come home until quite late. I could hear him singing off-key on his way back. Mother's annoyance had been rekindled by the sermon.

Coming home from church, she responded to a wave from Denis by muttering, "He must spend a lot of time in that silly thing. It's like a child playing house."

"There's nothing wrong with it," said Grandfather. "Denis has spent twenty-five years of his life at the beck and call of all kinds of people; now he just wants to sit by himself and think and read. I say, more power to him."

It looked to me as if most people resented Denis.

It started after he built the little house in the orchard. There was something frivolous about this, and everybody in the township liked practical things. Denis took a lot of chafing when he went to the village or even to church.

I detected traces of strange bitterness in the joking.

Then it happened!

On the way to school one morning I saw the building sprawled on its side. It looked like a strange, big bird that had crash-landed in the orchard.

Some of the children laughed; but I didn't feel like laughing, because I knew it was going to hurt Uncle Denis. The teacher shook her head when we spoke about it.

"That's a cruel thing to do."

It stayed there for several weeks. Somebody in the village said that the boys who had upset it wanted to come back and put it right. It looked accusing in the way it sprawled out in the grass growing up around it.

Denis left that summer and never came back.

Tom Henders bought the place that winter and he hauled the gazebo out of the orchard and boarded it up to make a brooder house. It was a strange-looking thing. I don't think I have ever been as happy as the day it burned down when the brooder stove exploded.

I don't think the gazebo was meant to be practical.

It was certainly a difficult thing to introduce in a community where hard work was equated with virtue. Both Methodists and Catholics were pleased to see the gazebo vanish, but I think they all felt a little guilty.

I remember my maternal grandmother mistily. It's like putting together a painting from fragments. The bits and pieces are the tiny memories of earliest childhood, tucked away so deeply in the memory bin that they're hard to get at. There was, for instance, the stately way she walked. Her head was always erect, supported, it seemed, by the high choker collar clutched at the neck with a large cameo pin. Her dress whispered as it parted to disclose the soft, black calf shoes and the place they started to lace. How high they were I never knew.

My grandmother wore her hair like a wreathed tiara of white silk caught with a speckled celluloid comb that had tiny brilliants in it. Once I saw her with the hair down, brushing the sheen of the silkiness.

"Grandma, your hair looks like a horse's tail."

For a moment I thought she was going to be angry, but she caught me up close to the stiff-looking bulwark of her front that turned out to be soft, and as she laughed I thought she smelled like clean wash on a clothesline. I knew she was old. People told me that, but her face was always pinky white and seemed more like the baby skin of my cousin than the wind-wrinkled skin of other old people.

There was a ceremonial in the way she put on an apron. It was always starched and frilly along the edges, and she tied the ends behind like big, fluffy handles. When she sat down in the rocking chair, her hands would smooth the apron down against the black, rustling dress, and then I could see the hands and the wrinkles and the small scaliness, and they looked old and made me sad inside in a way I couldn't understand.

"Now we can talk and rock," she would say, and the sad feeling would flit away.

She sat beside the window where she could watch the road. She had watched that road for many years, from the time when her husband used to work out to help pay for the first small farm up to this time when she watched for the first time when I came home, my coat torn, my nose bloody and my heart filled with the determination never to return to school. She was the one who had come running out to pick me up. She was the one who had wiped the tears and said, "If you don't go back tomorrow and face it, you'll never grow up to be a man like your grandfather."

She didn't say like any other man. To her there was no other man like her husband. She had waved me down the road the next morning, whispering in my ear, "If that boy is too big to slug, then rassle him down."

They used to say that she had once, as a young bride, chased a bear from the barnyard. No one confirmed it. She probably did. I know she punctured the seat of the pants of an amorous hired man one time with a five-tined manure fork.

It was hard to believe looking at her in the rocking chair looking out the window. I liked to watch her from a bumpy rag rug that I had to share with an aged and privileged cat. Sometimes her eyes would stray around the room, reliving the scenes associated with the objects collected over the years.

The room was fussy and cluttered and alive with glints of light from the nickel on the stove, the gilt on picture frames and the glasses and crockery ranged on the shelves of the breakfront. There was a footstool of green plush with curved legs of horn. Grandfather said they were buffalo horns. Grandmother cautioned me they were cow horns and said, "Don't let on you know. He's told that story so often he believes it himself."

There was a fat, pink shell that roared in your ear when you held it close to your head. Grandfather said it was the sound of the sea. My grandmother nodded her head and smiled when I asked her about it.

"It could be I suppose. I wouldn't know. I always wanted to hear the sea, but I guess it won't happen now."

That's when she took out the old, fat leather book and started to leaf through it. The leather cover was worn and scratched, and the leaves were loose with age. This book told about Killarney in County Kerry, and Grandmother yearned to see it. She talked about the place where her mother came from, and it was almost as if the years of listening and of leafing through the book had made her familiar with it. As she spoke of Lough Leane and Ross Castle and Muckross Abbey, the sound of it was a litany of longing.

The room was a shrine of mementos of shared sorrows and happiness. Here were the brownish-pink aged photos and tintypes of people starched into poses for studio photographs. The curved glass bell jar held a golden vase of flowers from her own wedding, artificial and ready to dissolve into dust if anyone had lifted the glass. A wisp of palm wound around the frame of a garishly bloody holy picture of anguish.

It was in this room that a wizened sweet potato yielded up from a desiccated skin a wondrous green vine that curled like a leafed snake over a sampler which proclaimed in stitched dots HOME SWEET HOME. Here was the somewhat tatty bearskin which I had fondly imagined was the hide of the one put to rout by Grandmother but which actually had been brought home from a store in northern Michigan by Grandfather when he left the log drive on the Saginaw River.

On a three-cornered table supported by three crossed bamboo sticks, colored black with gold stipples, there reposed a glass ornament which produced a snowstorm when it was tilted. It sat alongside a glass bar which had a scenic view of Niagara Falls on the bottom of it in such a way that it was magnified when you looked through the glass. The stereopticon with its double image had scenic shots, adventure shots, and startlingly realistic close-ups of animals.

Grandmother kept taffy in twisted spills of paper in a glass bowl on one of the lamp holders at the end of the organ. It was just high enough that I had to get a chair to reach it. There was a tacit agreement that I didn't touch it unless I was asked to. Once I saw it almost empty when the whole family assembled for Grandmother's birthday. There was lettering on the bottom of the bowl and a sketch of strange buildings. I always wanted to ask her what was on the bowl. Later, when it was passed, the anticipation of the candy made me forget to ask.

I remember arriving at her place one day in tears. Two of the Enver boys had been teasing me and calling me an "incense sniffer."

Grandmother smiled when I demanded in a mood of revenge, "The Methodists won't go to heaven, will they?"

I'm not sure it was said in revenge or fear of meeting my tormenters in the place of celestial glory. My grandmother handed me a photograph of a sweet-faced girl with a choker collar. At first I thought it was my grandmother, but she said, "That was my sister Hannah. She married a Methodist, and my family had conniptions."

She stared at it for a long while and then said, "I'm hoping to meet her soon in heaven. You see child, heaven is a place for all of God's children who try to live good lives."

There came a time when Grandmother was no longer at the rocker. She was in the front bedroom, and people, all the family, sat in the kitchen and in the parlor and there was scarcely a sound. I wanted to go in and see her, but my mother clenched my hand harder than usual and said I must be a good boy because Grandmother wasn't well.

I can remember the doctor coming in. I liked Dr. Jamieson because he had once given me candy, but his whiskers frightened me a little. He didn't look at me but went into the room, and I glimpsed my aunts around the big bed with the tall back that had wooden angels carved on it. When the door closed my heart started to thump, and I didn't have a reason for it. My aunts came out, and I could see they were crying. The doctor came out, and my grandfather came to the door and beckoned to me. When I went in, Grandmother was lying back on the pillow, and her face and the hair all streamed out seemed as white as the pillow. He took me close and put my hand on hers, and I felt the hardness of her rosary and the coldness of her hands. It frightened me until she smiled a little, and then before I could say anything he took me back to the front room.

We were there a long time, and I fell asleep. When I woke up the lamps were burning on the table and on the two holders of the organ. I saw the bowl on the table and when I went to it there was no candy in it. The door of the front room was open and I saw all of the family kneeling and there was a white sheet up over the pillow and I couldn't see Grandmother. The hired man was standing beside me and something prompted me to ask, "What does that say on the bowl?"

He leaned over and read slowly, "April 30–December 1,

1904." Then he coughed and stumbled over the words, "Louisiana Purchase Exposition." He added in a hoarse whisper, "That was the big World's Fair at St. Louis." I nodded, but finally understood why Grandmother treasured it as much for having been sent to her by her sister. I was thinking of what a big place heaven must be if God was going to take in both Methodists and Catholics.

CHAPTER 5

TOWN MICE AND COUNTRY MICE

The people of the village of Clover and the people of the township lived in what was normally a peaceful relationship. It was recognized that the village existed largely because of the patronage of the farmers in the area.

Town merchants were inclined to be somewhat resentful of people who ordered from mail-order houses.

In fact, Mr. Black the station agent, used to tuck mail-order packages away in the freight shed if any of the merchants were around at train time. Farmers with store bills would carefully throw a blanket or a robe over mail-order parcels and packages when they drove into the village from the station.

A certain proportion of the residents of the village were retired farmers. They never fully recovered from the revelation that many of their needs that had been supplied naturally on the farm cost money when they moved to Clover.

When they made their purchases they grumbled, especially when it came to such staples as eggs, butter, and meat. Most of them kept a cow at first, but as times changed they gave this up and bought milk. Finally they even succumbed to the lure of buying "baker's bread."

The retired Catholics adjusted to attending church in the

village. The white-brick Methodists found it harder to leave the tolerance of Reverend McPherson for the fundamentalist views of the pastor of the red-brick Methodist church in the village. In time, however, the warmth of his dissertations on the imminence of hell won them over. Most of them in the last lap of their lives found comfort in the strength of his convictions.

Winter was the difficult time for these people. It enforced hibernation when they were used to choring and activity.

The warming days of early May broke the bondage. The women scoured and polished on the outside. Rag rugs made splotches of bright color draped out of upstairs windows. Quilts and clothes were pegged to clotheslines for a spring airing.

Men, self-conscious of the size of their garden plots, but pleased and stirred by the smell of freshly turned earth, busied themselves with cultivating and planting. There was a new lift to their steps as they made frequent trips to the hardware store or the flour and feed store. There they discussed the merits of garden seeds in almost as serious a way as they once talked about the spring seeding of acres of land.

The flurry of work in early spring would peter out. There came a time when the garden was planted, the repairing and the painting and the tinkering were finished.

Then they started drifting to the livery stable. There was something obviously satisfying in the smell of harness, hay, and the sweat of horses. On upturned nail kegs they sat in the sun and indulged in that favorite of all sports, "horse talk."

"I remember the year I traded the little bay mare with the white stockings for a sorrel, with Pete Mills. Well, sir, that sorrel was a two-year-old, and I tell you now I never had a better horse on the place."

Another man, nodding, was waiting impatiently for his chance to start up a monologue of his own.

"You remember the people that lived on the Wales place across the river, down by the end of the third concession?"

He didn't wait for an answer.

"He had a big Percheron. A rawboned horse of five, going on six, and he liked this little chestnut mare of mine . . ."

The speaker cackled off in laughter at his own cunning in concealing the defects of the chestnut and gaining the big Percheron.

Some of them went to the implement dealers. They sat and watched as Jake fixed and repaired, and they itched to be given the chance of taking a hand. Just to help put new teeth in a harrow or a seat in the disk or grope around a broken seed drill seemed to give them a great sense of satisfaction.

Others had favorite seating spots in the cavernous blacksmith shop. Here they could participate in farm talk with men waiting for horses to be shod.

"Well, sir, the best team I ever had I used the year I broke up the old pasture next to the bush."

You found them at the flour and feed store.

"I think this sweet clover is going to be the ruination of farming. It's just going wild, and when it does it will be worse than wild mustard."

There were clover men.

"For feeding you can't beat clover. Red clover is the best feed you can get."

Some were timothy adherents.

"You take and cut timothy just at the right time and it's about the best all round feed you can have. Trouble is that people let it go too far. It gets woody."

They sat and watched fertilizer being unloaded. Some shook their heads at the thought of chemicals being introduced. In their days there had always been plenty of good barnyard manure.

It was good for a week of watching and pleasant pastime when a man brought a carload of western horses to the stock pens at the station. They sat and watched in deep concentration as the horses were gentled and broken and sold. Most of them, used to raising their own horses, felt that there was a great danger in this matter of bringing in "foreign" horses.

I had seen them as part of the life of the village. I hadn't thought about them until one day when my father made a hurried trip to the village. He was busy seeding and anxious to finish, hovering over the machinist who was welding the broken part.

As we came out, an elderly cousin approached. I walked on because I was certain my father would speak politely and hurry on home. Instead he stood and talked or, I should say, listened.

"This spring reminds me of the year I worked for your grandfather. Just about the same kind of weather. I remember we had a rough April and then it turned warm all of a sudden."

The cousin finally ran down like a phonograph spring, and Father said good-by to him and we left in the buggy.

"He wasted a lot of your time," I said.

He didn't say anything for several minutes. Finally he spoke. "For a man like Barney, spring is an anxious time. Just let's hope that when we're waiting for death, somebody stops to talk to us or even listen to us."

Then he added softly, "Especially in the spring when everything around you is so full of living."

Every trip to the village was a delight to a youngster. Country youngsters could be spotted by their porridge-bowl haircuts, cut-down clothes, and leathery faces with their usual assortment of freckles. They tended to stay together, invading Lee's Café for soda pop and eying the village gaffers who sat at tables.

We never thought of taking a table for a simple purchase of a bottle of cream soda. Somehow tables were associated with eating and most of us never had the capital or the nerve for a store-bought meal.

We bought coal oil in two-gallon cans at the store. There was a cap for the top opening and one for the small spout. The lid for the spout was soon lost, and sometimes it was replaced with a whittled plug of cedar. If this was lost the storekeeper would usually stick a gumdrop over it.

You could hardly wait to steal that gumdrop and eat it, coal-oil taste and all.

White cord in the stores was spun on paper cones that were usually purple in color. We prized those cones as miniature megaphones. Eventually they disintegrated because we chewed the small ends.

The metal tabs from plug tobacco were regarded as prizes by all boys. These were affixed to overall bibs as decorations, along with the occasional bottle cap reading CREAM SODA.

Automobiles were scarce, and it was a lucky boy who came into possession of an old tire. He enjoyed about the same level of prestige as the modern boy with a sports roadster.

Gauntlets were a positive mania. Most illustrations showed engineers of railroads wearing gauntlets, and we ached to get a pair. They were considered frivolous, so there was little possibility of getting a new pair. Sometimes, however, you could scrounge an old pair from the threshing-crew tank man, which you wore at the slightest provocation.

An old inner tube was a precious thing. It provided unlimited amounts of material for slingshots. It also came in handy for bartering. I remember once trading four rubber bands for a slightly used tie brought back from Detroit by the cousin of a schoolmate.

This tie was probably the forerunner of all the neon extravaganzas ever seen in the world. It combined the most vivid hues of reds, oranges, blues, and black. For almost a month I kept it hidden in a dresser drawer and then one Sunday put it on, keeping out of sight of my mother.

Grandfather took a look at it and raised his eyebrows in amazement. Mother noticed it about five minutes after we were inside the church. I don't think church did her much good that Sunday.

We were all fascinated by collector cards. In the early days of merchandising, someone discovered that people would buy products simply for the sake of the enclosures. There were cards of babies, animals, birds, flowers, sports, plants, trees, and ballplayers that we didn't know about.

In our household there were no purchases made simply because of the pictures; my collection was a limited one.

I used to inspect the baking-powder box each week, but the contents went down at a terribly slow rate, leaving me with only the pictures of a cardinal and a robin in a period of some six months.

There were paper cutouts on cornflake boxes, but we had cornflakes only on Sunday or when there were visitors. I didn't get many of them.

Our mothers wore freshly laundered and ironed print dresses to the village on Saturday night. The village women always seemed to be dressed for church, even on nonspecial occasions.

Our fathers wore second-best clothes on Saturday night, usually with a light shirt and a collar stud, but seldom yielding to a stiff collar. The banker, the insurance agent, the clergymen, and many others wore what seemed to be good suits all the time.

The ability to talk to girls was something the village lads acquired at an early age. They clustered in front of the hall, by the war memorial, or at the bridge over the river near the gristmill. The talk seemed to flow easily.

Our parents marked the girls as "saucy and fresh," but how we envied those boys their free and easy conversational graces.

Country boys had a tendency to run in packs, and the girls went in giggling coveys. Older boys clustered in front of the feed store or the blacksmith shop and pretended to talk about work and farming, but it was easy to see that they eyed the girls at every opportunity.

The bank was a mysterious place of oiled floors, frosted glass, brass-rodded cages, and oaken counters. A formidable sign in large letters that proclaimed PRIVATE marked the manager's office.

I always resented the fact that my father, normally a man of affairs and resolution around the farm and in his daily work, seemed to be hesitant when it was time to make a trip into that inner sanctum. If he came out scowling, I kept quiet. If he came out smiling and smoking a cigar, it was my signal to ask for a nickel. I always got it too.

The harness maker, the blacksmith, and the feed-store men seemed to be more like country people. They talked the same language as my father and my grandfather.

The butcher had a small shop where the floor was covered with wood shavings. The blinds were drawn in the summertime and it gave the illusion of coolness. In the shop he wore a sailor hat of straw, summer and winter, and a bloody apron drawn around a big paunch. He wore blue shirts and startling white, stiff collars and small red bow ties.

He had a slaughterhouse out past where the Jenks family lived by the village dump. On Thursdays, he closed shop and went into the country to do custom butchering for farmers. This was still in the days when many farmers pickled meat, smoked some of it, and fried down side meat in crocks.

At the time I didn't realize it, but the village was changing.

The lean-to beside the blacksmith shop was catering to automobiles. Merchants were scandalized because some of the local people were driving to the county town of Handrich to shop on Saturday night.

That was nothing compared with the talk when a local farmer took his wife to Detroit for a week of holidays. Before that, such a trip would have to coincide with a family wedding or bereavement.

The local baker started rumors that the bread being imported from the county town bakeshop was dangerous because of the wax-paper wrapping.

Village youths brought girls to dances in the township hall. Country boys took country girls to dances in the village hall. Whenever the twain were mixed, trouble usually ensued, although it was a known fact that many of the country girls were fickle enough to be enticed by the village lads who were driving motor cars.

When Clover, which was not incorporated, became involved as a formal village, a lot of things took place. One of them had to do with regular garbage collection, for which a nominal charge was made. This was coupled with a threat from a newly appointed district health officer, who frowned on the habit of throwing garbage on the village dump or putting it in shallow holes on vacant lots.

The motor car was becoming accepted, and a new diversion grew up. Some village people discovered that they could combine Sunday evening drives to the country with garbage disposal. Wrapping the stuff in old newspapers, they wheeled merrily along the roads, heaving packages as they went.

I suppose there was a certain amount of sportsmanship in it, because they seemed to take a particular delight in trying to hit an ornamental fence along the front of Jimmy Janes' place. He was a bachelor who lived on a quiet side road with only one neighbor, and he prided himself on the rather ornate fence which his father bought from a property in Handrich, where the house had burned down. It was iron curlicued and doo-dadded.

Jimmy stood it as long as he could, and then when he heard that an impromptu contest had been arranged with several village parties due to converge on a certain Sunday evening, he called in reinforcements. There was a problem, however. Jimmy was a self-acknowledged atheist. He had written several letters to the Clover *Clarion* on the subject and once went all the way to Chicago to attend a convention of atheists.

The arguments raged hot and heavy over whether or not to help him. Some felt it was lending credence to his beliefs which Catholic and Methodist alike abhorred. Just the same, Clover township came through with flying colors.

Every young lad in the township, and a lot of the older men as well, went along. I sneaked from home and became a spectator. Just before dusk, the cars wheeled in from the county road and started down the side road. There were about eight cars in the party, and as they came abreast of the gateway they started firing the barrage. Then a horn blew as the first one came to a barricade of brush on the road, and this was the signal for the defenders to rise up from behind the fence on Jimmy's side and from the scrub willows on the other side.

How the ammunition flew! Overripe tomatoes, rotten eggs, juicy plums, corncobs, cow flaps, balls of feathers, and roofing tar. It was a scene that would make movie "Cowboys and Indians" look insignificant.

Women were screaming. Drivers trying to turn their cars around were backing into the soft side of the road and getting stalled. The defenders withdrew in true guerrilla fashion, leaving the scene of carnage. Jimmy was a good host, and Father didn't come home until very late.

That stopped the garbage-disposal business, but it certainly strained district and village relationships for some time.

Jimmy reciprocated. On the following Sunday morning he raised quite a stir by attending Mass at St. Peter's. Everybody flocked around him, trying to make him welcome. It was quite an accomplishment to have a real atheist attending the Catholic church.

That evening, however, he attended service at the white-brick church, and the Methodists were shocked into a form of pleasure. All church people pondered about where he would go the following Sunday.

Having performed the generous gesture Jimmy stayed at home after that.

CHAPTER 6

CARDS, CULTURE, AND CHANGE

While the winter winds skiltered across the frozen landscape of our township and tried to sneak through cracks and crevices, most of the inhabitants indulged in playing cards. Not all, mind you! There were still some, mindful of the fundamentalism of the circuit riders, who associated round dancing and playing cards with works of the devil.

Grandfather was a euchre player! In his own mind he was a veritable champion, playing with verve and skill, so that if he happened to lose there was always a sound reason, if not a series of reasons.

The euchre enthusiasts were many, and with them it was euchre all the time! They fumed with impatience when people suggested other games, such as five hundred, hearts, or fish, but might be induced to play an occasional game of rummy if the required four people didn't happen to be available.

I preferred playing rummy to euchre. Grandfather would agree to play, but as soon as the first game was over he started hinting, "Euchre is a better game." I always had to give in, and after sorting the cards we played two-handed euchre.

Then Grandfather started to beam. "This is a real game."

It would seesaw back and forth between us. I often wondered about my grandfather during one of these sessions. How could this man who was known as a daredevil on the log drive, who walked like a cat on the framework of a barn during a framing, and who was said to have had nerves of steel get so worked up when he was losing a simple euchre game?

Mother made furious motions at me if I were winning because she knew it distressed him, but some of the fever caught me as well, and there were times when I pursued him with every advantage that luck gave. I had to depend on luck because my skill couldn't stand up to his ability and experience.

During stormy winter days, there was a general impression that if you couldn't find a storekeeper, you might find him playing cards. There were several haunts for the men. Red Sandy Macdonald, Black Jack McCarthy, and my grandfather used to play with Hjalmar Olsen in the "Smoke Hole," a carefully hidden room at the back end of the cavernous blacksmith shop.

Another group played in the back room of Ab Walker's Furniture and Undertaking Parlor if he didn't have a corpse on hand. There was a continuous game going on at the barbershop behind a flimsy curtain which had been erected out of respect for several devout Methodist elders who frowned on euchre.

Gambling was, by and large, a minor factor in the matter of euchre. Our people played cards because it was a time-passer and because they played with fervor that made up in most cases for skill. A game of euchre with my grandfather and Hjalmar Olsen opposing Red Sandy Macdonald and Black Jack McCarthy was a roaring, bluffing, and argumentative affair.

They pounded the table with their fists when they took

tricks, argued about points to a state bordering on apoplexy, signaled furiously, and were not above edging their counters from time to time. They sounded like the bitterest of enemies and yet continued to play every winter and managed to stay boon companions.

The euchre fever came about the time of the first snow. You could tell Grandfather had caught it when he picked up his plate at suppertime and made vague gestures of helping my mother with the dishes.

"Oh, Pa, go and sit down," she would exclaim, "I know what you're up to."

"Just because I offer to help you a bit, you start complaining."

Then she laughed, "I guess we might have a game of euchre tonight, but mind you, not too late. This one has to go to school tomorrow."

Before the last dish was put away, he was shuffling the cards at the table. "Just two out of three," he announced as I slipped in to be his partner.

It stretched into three out of five and finally into five out of seven, and then we lost count. Finally Mother would look up at the clock and exclaim in a horrified tone, "Look at the time."

Just the same she always made a pot of cocoa and some sandwiches, and as we sat and ate them, Grandfather recalled all his brilliant plays. Mother looked amused, but Father was inclined to argue, and I have heard them coming up the front stairs to bed still nibbling at each other. If I listened carefully I might hear Mother say to Father, "Why do you act so silly? Pa just likes to win." Father would grumble off to sleep, and by next morning, it would be forgotten.

During the winter there were large-scale euchre parties, to say nothing of informal parties of a table or two that were constantly being organized. At home there was scarcely a night in the dead of winter when someone didn't come in for "cards." A bachelor neighbor might stroll over after supper or a hired man from a neighboring farm where playing cards was still not admitted, and Grandfather would strain the leash of his patience while the usual small talk went on.

"Like a game of euchre?"

Then they were at it. I watched at first and then slipped back to the rocking chair in front of the stove and scrunched down, hoping that no one would notice me. If I was lucky, and Mother was playing, I tried to stay up until there was lunch. Sometimes I was sent down to draw a pitcher of icy cider from the barrel in the cold room of the basement or bring a plate of Spy apples that fairly snapped with brittleness when you bit into them.

With the firelight flickering from the open damper of the stove and the shadows of the players against the lamplight, the old cat idling his motor beside the wood box and the dog muttering through dreams on the rug in front of the oven door, it was one of those scenes that remain in memory for all time.

The big card parties were usually held on a Friday night. The Oddfellows alternated with the Catholics in sponsoring them. There were usually twelve tables with forty-eight players, a good number of children who played and rough-housed in the furnace room, and some women with small children and older women who sat at the back of the hall and gossiped.

About ten o'clock a lunch of salmon sandwiches, along with tea and coffee laced with milk and sugar, was served. We crammed ourselves, golluping the tea or coffee out of sight of our parents.

Usually, by the time we were leaving for home, I could

hardly keep my eyes open; but I remember one night when the air was electric. Grandfather was snappy mad and Father was whistling and I knew Mother was on guard for trouble. Not a word was spoken until we started into the frosty length of the Big Swamp. Father put his head up and sniffed.

"Smell anything, Harry?"

"No," I said innocently.

"Funny," he said, "I thought I smelled skunk."

Mother poked at him, but he was armor-plated in a horsehide coat and Grandfather grumbled like a wounded lion.

"Damned cheats."

Grandfather, not making a point, had been skunked at a game. He stayed home Saturday night, went grumbling to Mass on Sunday, and didn't budge out of the house on Monday.

All day Monday he kept saying that the older Methodists who abhorred cards were right. It was a fact that euchre made some people dishonest. My mother just looked amused, and that raised his choler even more. By Tuesday the euchre fever returned, and he hitched a ride to Clover on a sleighload of logs.

He came home in full glee. "By George we had a wonderful game."

Mother's eyebrows shot up. "I thought you agreed with the Methodists about not playing cards."

"Well," he mumbled, "my partner was John Willy Smith —and he's a Methodist."

Mother started to say something. I think she was going to remind him that John Will hadn't been in a church for years, much to the dismay of his own mother, but she just said in her noncommittal but diplomatic way, "Well, that was nice."

You might say Clover was a well-knit community when I was a boy. A few strangers, and there weren't many, slipped into the pattern of living without too much fuss.

But now and then one came along who fought the customs, and the results were sometimes tragic and often amusing.

Mrs. Henderson, a frothy-looking woman with piled-up hair, was determined to make over our place. She was a city girl, tolerated for the most part because her banker husband controlled a good deal of the credit in the township.

A week after she arrived, the Clover *Clarion* printed her picture in a cartwheel hat and said she looked forward to living in the village and hoped to encourage a cultural upsurge. She was interested in music, drama, and folk songs.

Grandfather threatened to call on her and recite some of his lumberjack ballads or invite her to a "wet" evening at the Smoke Hole in back of Olsen's Blacksmith Shop. But Mother threatened him in turn with all kinds of punishment.

We didn't know very much about culture, except the kind they talked about at the cheese factory. The item caused a lot of talk for a time, but it died down.

There was a concert after the fowl supper and we heard a piano player, a very loud female singer, a harmonica quartet, a fiddle player who didn't play a recognizable tune, and a man with a deep voice who sucked in a moth at one point and was considered the highlight of the affair.

They were from Handrich, the county town, and were hired because the Methodists didn't believe in having a dance and you couldn't just close up after the supper.

By the time we got around to the Christmas concerts at the various churches and schools that only varied in structure, content, and performance by the difference in the two

Santa suits available, most people had forgotten about Mrs. Henderson. She was busy, however!

She persuaded Mr. McPherson, a dour Scots minister, to allow the Swiss Bell Ringers to put on a concert. It was a great success, and Mrs. Henderson made a speech in which she promised real cultural entertainment for Clover.

We heard a lot of rumors. It was apparent that Mrs. Henderson was organizing something special. She ferreted out almost everybody in the township who ever had any musical training. Of course most of the best locals played by ear. She didn't want them, because it seems she had written some music. Somebody said she had sent it to Ernest MacMillan (that was before he was knighted), and he wrote back and said he had never seen a score like it before.

She had Agatha Simms, a retired singer with a mad passion for flying, and all the local music teachers to her house for afternoon tea.

She took over the Oddfellows Hall and borrowed Jake Deegan, the handyman who looked after the bank, to rig up a stage.

Mr. Henderson took to visiting the back room of the Commercial Hotel because his wife had turned his house into a rehearsal hall. Most of the regulars said that after a few belts of brew he was quite a likable fellow and quite different from the austere banker who questioned them so sharply when they wanted a loan.

Then one day a lean, sallow-faced man with long gray hair and dark pouches under his eyes came in on the afternoon train from Toronto. He wore a gray plug hat and a cape and carried a cane with silver knob. He registered at the Commercial and said he was Cecil Hubert Fotheringham, an actor.

He ate his meals, except breakfast, which he missed, at

the banker's home and sent the bill for his room to Mrs. Henderson. George Warner wouldn't charge drinks in the back room, because of the Canada Temperance Act, I guess, but the actor didn't go shy because he evidently had a vast repertoire of bawdy verses which he found no difficulty in exchanging for the hospitality of the other visitors.

The *Clarion* ran an advertisement for "An Evening of Varied Cultural Entertainment," and handbills appeared in all the stores and the post office. There were to be ensembles, trios, and solo performances of readings and music. No one would admit that they were going, but everyone knew that the place was going to be packed.

Some people worried about it happening in Lent. Others thought seventy-five cents for adults and forty cents for children was a bit steep. It didn't hold down attendance, however, because the hall was packed.

There was a stage with a velvet curtain drawn across it, bearing the arm and hammer emblem of Clover, later identified as a trademark for washing soda. There were footlights made out of tin cans and gasoline lamps on both sides of the hall.

People kept poking their heads out between the folds of the curtain, and at one point it collapsed, sending about a dozen people on the stage scrambling into the wings.

It took some time to get the curtain back up on the wire, but finally Mrs. Henderson came out and made a speech. She had a long dress on that showed a lot of her top and made some of the women in the audience fidget and whisper. Then the curtains jerked apart and we saw what was supposed to be the ensemble.

"Chicken Jimmy" Wilks, who had flunked out of the second-year poultry course at Ontario Agricultural College, was waving a stick in front of them. It was the composition by Mrs. Henderson called "Clover Number One." Gramp said it was named after a grass seed. Jimmy Henderson, who was playing a thing called a bull fiddle, played for about a minute after everyone else finished.

Agatha Simms sang "Trees," which was well received, and besides, everybody liked her.

Then Cecil Hubert Fotheringham came out in a funny suit with long stockings and a feathered hat and carried a thin sword and went on and on reciting something that nobody knew, but he jumped around a lot and seemed to be fighting with something imaginary.

Mrs. Henderson sang what she called an aria which was pretty high and gave me a headache. A Swiss fellow from the cheese factory played the accordion and yodeled. The musical ensemble came back and played some more and it wasn't bad because you could almost recognize some of the tunes.

The actor recited some Shakespeare which was all about murder and sleep. "Chicken Jimmy" played a sad piece on the violin, and then Mrs. Henderson came out again.

She said it was a shame that folk songs were being neglected and that she had a treat for the audience. A local resident was going to sing some treasures in this field.

Grandfather sat up and opened his eyes, and out stepped "Sheep Willy" Jenks, the chieftain of a clan who lived in a ramshackle collection of rooms beside the village dump. He was dressed up in one of the banker's suits, and he even had a necktie on with the knot hanging in midair between his Adam's apple and his navel. His son Bert brought out a guitar and, "Sheep Willy" brushed his whiskers and proceeded to sing "The Jam on Garry's Rocks."

It was pretty good, and when all that applause rolled in he bowed and started in to sing something called "Black-Eyed Tess."

That broke up the concert. Mothers started hauling their youngsters out. But "Sheep Willy" kept right on to the end.

The concert was the main topic of talk for a week. The next Saturday night when our folks were going to confession, Rosie Glynn came out smiling and announced in a loud whisper: "You don't have to tell about going to the concert in Lent. Father Morrison says it was no sin to listen to Sheep Willy's song. Just going to the concert was penance enough."

That about finished culture in Clover!

After that we went back to dances, especially in the township. There was a tacit agreement that the young people from the white-brick Methodist church would attend dances as long as there was a sprinkling of square dances to command the attention of the older people who came along ostensibly as chaperones.

In the beginning the music was supplied locally.

Red Sandy, a careless farmer, was an enthusiastic fiddler. His musical education was scarce, and he played by ear, fortified by hard cider to the point where enthusiasm overcame a lack of knowledge.

Milly Simpson was a music teacher. About almost every boy and girl in the township at one time or another faced the ordeal of music lessons. Most of them lasted about four trips.

Milly supplemented her teaching by playing the organ in the church on the fourth concession and renting her piano at five dollars a night for the township hall dances.

This was considered a bit high, and so by common agreement she was asked to play it as well.

The rest of the orchestra just happened. Ab Crich played a harmonica. Several volunteers supplemented the music by playing on Jew's harps.

Albert, a local who spent most of his time working hard

to get out of manual labor had a sort of ear for music. At one time or another he had experimented with almost all known instruments. He started on the ocarina, known as the "sweet potato." When a music school was set up in town he was one of the first to buy a Hawaiian guitar. He paid so much a week and was entitled to a lesson with each payment.

Albert gave up the guitar. In fact the salesman went out of business or at least moved to another town, when the twenty-odd bachelor students discovered that his so-called "daughter" with the bleached-blond hair was really his wife. A medicine show, stranded one time in the village, sold Albert a drum and a set of traps.

Drumming was too hard work for Albert. He traded the set for a heifer calf to Joe McCabe.

When Red Sandy wanted to be relieved at the fiddle he would turn it over to Ab Mackay. Ab knew only one number, and so the crowd might have to dance two or three times to "The Wind That Shakes the Barley," until Sandy returned.

There were two-steps, waltzes, square dances, an occasional schottische. The Grand Promenade was played at lunchtime (midnight), and Red Sandy always played a tearful "Auld Lang Syne" to close the affair. The square dances were danced with great enthusiasm, and we had some excellent callers in the township.

It was strange, but Albert, the man who hated work, was the cause of the breakdown in our township hall dances. He introduced the radio to our valley and older folks started getting interested in listening. They would congregate at my uncle's store, where he had installed an extra speaker from the set in the kitchen. Soon quite a few had radios at home, and while this broke up some of the conversation parties at the general store, it had another and unexpected effect.

The younger members of the township families grew dissatisfied with the makeshift orchestra. They were hearing tunes on the radio that Red Sandy didn't know, and it became apparent that there wasn't a great deal of variety in his playing.

This was 1927, and change was in the air. Toronto had its new Union Station opened by the Prince of Wales. We heard on the radio about the collapse of George Young and the win by Vierkoetter in the Wrigley Swim.

The banker had paid over $900 for a Chrysler car. Grandfather was quite upset by the fact that when he was in Toronto with the drover to sell cattle they had paid over fifty cents apiece to see a movie with Dorothy Gish.

In the light of so much progress, it was bound to happen. The Young Farmers' Club hired an outside orchestra to play for a dance. Red Sandy was shattered, and we thought he might not attend. He turned up, however, and sat glumly watching at the back of the hall while the Listowel Lads set up.

They had music stands and they wore blue jackets and white trousers. Even the pianist had a blue jacket and white skirt. They had a piano, two saxophones, a banjo, accordion, and drums. The strange absence was that of a fiddle. The leader was a saxophone player.

Red Sandy was disgusted and named them "the gurglers." He said they sounded like cows stuck in the mud.

CHAPTER 7

SCHOOL AND TEACHERS

There were two people in our community exposed directly to the Catholics and the Methodists on an equal basis who could tell you that religion had little to do with common characteristics. They were the respective teachers in the separate school attended by the Catholics and the public school attended by the Protestants.

The teachers came and worked and moved on. Some married in the township, and others couldn't wait until the end of the year to shake the dust of the place from their heels. There were farm girls hoping for husbands, town girls with romantic ideas about the country, and city girls who for the most part were completely baffled by the whole setup.

Schoolteachers were expected to be decorous, thrifty, modest in speech and dress, miracle workers as far as backward children were concerned, firm disciplinarians over unruly boys, dispensers of worldly wisdom for girls approaching puberty, and magicians as far as talent for a Christmas concert was concerned. They were expected to work for the lowest sum possible, be polite to a penurious school board, listen to all the school-district gossip but never repeat any of it and dance with anyone who asked them at a party. It was generally agreed they must be tee-

totalers or that if they did take a drink it was forced on
them by a respected but imbibing member of the community . . . but only at home!

The schoolteacher usually was expected to board at the
home of the secretary-treasurer, or, if that was not possible,
the billet went to a relative. They were expected to accept
whatever fortune brought them in the way of cooking.
Sometimes they were lucky and sometimes they were not. A
female schoolteacher coming to our community was a virtual prisoner of the local mores. For a nominal sum of
thirty-five cents to cover the extra food she could invite a
suitor to her boardinghouse for dinner, unless it happened
to be a single relative of the family. Then it was free! She
could entertain on Sunday evenings in the chilly parlor if
the light was kept at a decent wick height. When the man
of the house dampered the kitchen stove for the night it
was generally accepted as being a cue for the young man to
go home.

The schoolteacher in the separate school was expected to
teach catechism and prepare the First Communion and
Confirmation classes under the direction of the parish
priest. The teacher at the public school had to be a prime
mover in the matter of Sunday school and Young Church
People. Schoolteachers were also expected to help school
trustees write speeches for office as municipal councilors,
officials of the Beef Ring, the Oddfellows, the Masons, the
Holy Name Society, the Elks, and the Orange Lodge.

The schoolteacher was expected to be a wizard at fashioning a scanty amount of crepe paper into decorations for
strawberry festivals, fowl suppers, and box socials. She
might find herself called upon to write an answer to the
most dreaded thing of all in the country . . . a lawyer's
letter, thereby saving the recipient a fee for having another
lawyer reply. She had also to be aware of the fact that dur-

ing the winter months, when she received a telephone call from her family or a friend, her call had the highest priority of any on the party line. The number of receivers down, at times caused the volume of the voices to be so low that one or two of the more magnanimous listeners would hang up of their own volition.

A teacher could be driven from the community by a cruel practical joke. A local public school teacher, who became known as "Miss Fizz," provided an example of this. She happened to be staying with a local Methodist family. She was a city girl and, to add to the tension, a Presbyterian with strong views in favor of Church Union.

Her host, Mr. Railer, was annoyed by her arguments and more aggravated by her habit of not patronizing the outdoor privy but making use of the white chamber pot under her bed. He considered this to be coddling and weakness. When she started going out with a young Catholic in the community, it made him furious.

He took individual packets of seidlitz powders and poured them into the dry "jerry." As he related with glee later, he lay in bed and waited. He heard the crockery being smuggled out from under the bed and later a scream that must have warmed his heart. The teacher is reported to have thought she was the victim of a gunpowder blast. Her host added to her chagrin by suggesting it might have been caused by "something she et."

She left shortly afterward, and Mr. Railer was not too popular when they had to send the children to the separate school for two months before they could get a replacement for "Miss Fizz."

Janitors were a risky business in our school. Most of the teachers had to be prepared to sweep and dust and even start fires. On more than one occasion I had come early to school to find a teary-eyed girl with the frozen water pail on the stove, fanning at the fire trying to get it going because the so-called janitor that morning had either forgotten to come or had more pressing work somewhere else.

Our teachers had to cope with classes that ranged from primer students to entrance classes. While a little lad would be wrestling with his alphabet, the first book puzzling over two and two, the second book trying to fathom a fable, the third book wrestling with grammar . . . the fourth-book students might be trying to assimilate facts concerning the repeal of the Corn Laws.

In addition to this the teachers had to work in one-room boxes that felt like refrigerators in the wintertime and ovens in the summertime. They had to cope with everything from spitballs that mysteriously appeared on the ceilings to deep-carved initials on desks that looked like pock-marked veterans after a few years. They had big boys who only went to school in the wintertime and could deftly snag a girl's pigtail in an inkwell or put the cap end of a twenty-two shell on a hot stove and lie cheerfully about it afterward.

Our teachers were supervisors of an untamed quarter-acre or so of schoolyard that ran rank with blue devils and burdocks and was given a cursory cutting in late August by a school trustee who wanted to earn a couple of dollars. Since the yard was uneven, he kept the cutter bar of the mower up high leaving the thick, spiked stalks of the burdocks like obstacles on a commando course. Since there was no appropriation for playground equipment, she was expected to beg, borrow, or steal a bat and ball. The students pleaded with her constantly to play with them, and if she entered into the game with abandonment she was liable to censure for acting as a tomboy and not giving a good example for the girls.

During class she played a steady and nerve-frazzling game with a procession of boys and girls who snapped their fingers with the request, "Please, may I go outside?" She had to have the wisdom of Solomon in trying to adjudge their need, because woe betide her if she made a mistake. She was also aware that they played the game of trying to confuse her memory so that two of them might be outside at the same time.

Our country teachers had to be masters of elementary first aid. There was a constant stream of boys and girls with scratches and bruises of various kinds. She had to overlook minor fights and be prepared to settle major ones. On a rainy day she sat upstairs in uneasy tension while the students played in the basement where the cordwood was rearranged and displaced for various purposes . . . much of which she wouldn't even let herself think about.

Thinking of them now, both Catholic and Protestant, I can only offer a belated word of sincere congratulation for their fortitude and understanding. I think of the very backward boy who came to our school. He had a habit of staring, and even when the teacher spoke to him, it took time to bring him back to the world of reality. He walked in a strange and misgaited way, never quite responding to the world around him. At first some of the children had a habit of picking on him, and one day, when this teacher spoke to him and he didn't answer, a little girl in the first book asked, "What's wrong with him, Miss?" The teacher held up her hand and said gently, "He's listening to God." It's a tribute to the teacher for the way she spoke and to herself as one of those individuals who taught us with wisdom under adverse circumstances that not a child in the room, from primer to fourth book, laughed or even smiled. They understood!

At both schools, Friday afternoon after recess time was devoted to art. The younger students drew in their scribblers, the more advanced ones in the small art books and the third and fourth book students went in for an orgy of color. Most of the boys and girls came in before the bell had summoned them back from recess. There was a great amount of preparation in filling clean ink bottles with water and getting a rag for cleaning the brush.

I wonder what a modern gallery director might think of our efforts. There were some strange concepts about shapes and colors. Students also varied in their application to art. The girls were mainly dainty and precise. The boys were inclined to slap colors on with the same abandonment as might be used in covering a barn, a fence, or a tool shed. In each lesson at least three ink bottles of water would be spilled. Several boys would lose their interest in painting on the page and turn to complicated tattoo designs on the back of their hands or else on the necks of the pupil who sat ahead.

We drew yellow and orange suns with startling spokes radiating in anything from green to violet skies. Our laneways had rail fences of nutty brown or black and trees that looked like patchwork quilts. Cows with frightening tails, sprawled legs, and weird horns stood in pastures or by ponds that resembled lunar lakes. We smudged and spilled and groped for expression confined to the dullness of a course of study book or whatever a desperate teacher conjured up in the faint hope that it might help us to get through an examination.

At entrance time we had to submit a portfolio of sketches and paintings and write an examination, if I remember correctly, about so-called picture study. The examiners were compassionate and you had to be a real dunce to fail.

Looking back on it now, it seems strange that we were confined to art appreciation in such a pedestrian way. Surrounding us was some of the greatest natural art it is possible to find. Every snowstorm brought a new and changing world. The sifting curtains of snow that slithered down to earth covered the starkness of the winter world and brought new accents in the dramatic contrast of black and white. An open patch of water under the creek bridge seemed to be moving, black velvet against the white snow. A line of tracks across the brow of a hill gave a startling effect. The pinched dots of the rabbits under the apple trees looked like exclamation marks. Soft snow puffed up on stack, barn, and tree until it seemed as if the magical land of fairy stories had come true.

The greatest teacher of all was the wind that took a hand in the redistribution of the snow. It ridged across the valleys and left stiff, whipped furrows on the side of the hills. It swept the snow up around the rail fences and skittered in amongst the dead weeds until only their tops stood out like abstract sculptures. We didn't know what abstract was in those days, but we were surrounded by nature's abstractions all the time. A blackened tree stump, the jagged edges of a trunk slashed by summer lightning, or an age-wearied barn that leaned were all true forms that took on new meaning by the simple way that snow swirled and piled around them.

We looked at frost crystals and forms on icy windows and marveled without knowing their artistic worth. Icicles glittered from house and barn eaves, changing even as they dripped. Soft days and zero nights after a snowstorm decorated the evergreens with their own kind of cascading ice forms. A moving winter moon of steely light brought forth a pantomime of changing forms and shapes and shadows on the snow. When you walked you were in a three-dimensional world of sound, sight, and feeling, with everything from the crunch of frost-infested snow to the withered hoot of the owl. There was a kind of loneliness of feeling in the vastness of the night that must surely have been a form of art appreciation.

The wind was an artist. On nights when we had a powdery skift of snow, the wind must have played all night, shifting and changing with each vagary of motion. You found it ridged in through a crack by the door, and it was piled up against the outside like weatherstripping. There were shadow drifts by the side of the woodpile, the saw-horse and even latticed ones that traced the slats of the gateway. The strawy wig of the stack would be powdered and iced and the leftover whisked in a knife-shaped draft, like the last swirl your mother used in decorating a cake. The wind poked and fingered at every crack and crevice, leaving tiny drifts inside to remind you of your own vulnerability or carelessness.

If we had only realized it at the time, we could have learned a great deal about composition. The wind, using only white snow, could compose some dramatic contrasts. An ugly slash of gravel pit or earth or even an earth scar would be partially covered, with only enough left open to make a vivid picture. Implements left out in the open were a real invitation for handiwork. The wind tucked it up here and scattered it there, fingering tongues and spoke wheels and skirling the snow off into sharp, blunt, and sometimes circling ridges.

The open surface of the pond we had cleared for skating gave the artist of nature a chance to make patterns of slim drifts and open spaces on the ice. On the flat fields beside the bush it scoured the snow down to a thin layer leaving the designs of weeds and tall grasses, that even looked like some of our pencil scratching on the art papers at school.

The wind also had a sense of humor. It liked to tuck snow up around the eaves of small, fat houses, making them look like roofed snowbanks. It whipped with fury at the snow and took it all away from tall, ugly houses leaving them raw, bare, and uglier than ever. It stole the snow from the open spaces of roadway and spilled it and jam-packed it into the hill cuts where it remained, packed ever harder by the hoofs of the horses until it became a mass of ice that stood as a monument to winter long into the warming days of spring when the rest of the roads had dried to dust.

There was an old covered bridge in a nearby township where the wind vented artistic fury. The icy fingers tried to swirl through the dark tunnel and ended up by packing each end with tremendous drifts that called for the road superintendent to come out after almost every storm. On the other hand it kept the slim steel open bridge on the Maitland swept clear all winter. It helped us when we built crude snow horses of jagged blocks by powdering the crevices and leaving the surface smooth and polished.

Meanwhile on wintry Friday afternoons, while the wind pulled, pushed, tugged, and blew the snow around outside the one-room schoolhouse, trying to attract our attention to the artistic perfections and designs of its own creation, we struggled with the world of crayon and water color. How I wish now one teacher had closed the course of study, made us put away the crayons, ink, bottles of water, and unrealistic colors and had introduced us to the world of pure abstraction afforded by the wind of winter playing with the flexible and decorative snow.

CHAPTER 8

TO KILL A MOOSE

Hunting was always associated with the fall season. You started with a slingshot and fired at almost anything. You could send a flight of sparrows shivering into the sky with a well-placed shot into a shade tree. Rusted signs on the ends of barns, the jagged edges of broken windows in deserted houses, or the green insulators on telephone poles were considered fair game.

Yappy dogs went howling with the pinch of a sharp stone from a catapult. You even set out bravely to bring down a woodchuck or a rabbit, but these creatures were too agile for that kind of primitive marksmanship. Later on you were privileged to accompany an older boy who owned a .22 rifle on a so-called hunt that consisted of a great deal of walking, resting, and talking, but very little hunting. You gaspered along behind his big strides with a stick in your hands, trying desperately to keep up and make believe you were a real hunter.

When the rabbits grew too thick in the township, there might be a drive by villagers and farmers both. They fanned out along the county line and advanced like a line of infantrymen, carrying everything from flintlocks to shotguns with a few muzzle-loaders dug up from dusty attics or driving sheds. The men wore bulky mackinaws and cut-down horse-hide coats with pockets large enough to accommodate shells in one and a bottle in the other. The frozen plowed fields were uneven and rough, and the men started out bravely to kind of roll over the clods of iron earth. By the end of the afternoon they were stumbling and falling, and it was perhaps only by the efforts of the prayerful wives at home and the grace of God that none suffered more than flesh wounds.

The rabbits meanwhile headed for haven miles away, mostly unscathed. We had few rabbits in Clover township, in spite of their natural instincts for propagation, for at least two years after each shoot.

In the fall there was a great shebang about coons. Men, accompanied by baying dogs of all kinds, most of whom had no desire to tangle with any wild animal, assembled beside a large bonfire on the flats. There they fortified themselves with a mixture of something called a "hot toddy" heated beside the bonfire in an old iron cooking pot.

It would be a night when straying black clouds played a game of hide-and-seek with an autumnal moon. The air was clean, crisp, and fresh except for an occasional whiff from the tannery. After a great deal of fussing, stamping of feet and blowing on hands some of the group would start out. Others would stay to keep the iron pot warm and some thought the cold earth a place soft enough for a nocturnal snooze.

You could hear that rag-taggle army of hunters for miles on the night air. They were mostly looking for lost dogs, coaxing dogs to get a bit of spirit into the affair, or bellowing what were supposed to be coon calls. Once they shot a coon, and several times they shot dogs belonging to other hunters, occasioning bad feelings for years, especially when a Catholic dog was shot by a Methodist hunter or vice versa.

The hunting news which transfixed the community was the time we heard that Jake Miller, the insurance man, and George Warner from the Commercial Hotel were planning a moose hunt! This was startling! The only time most of us had ever seen a moose was in a natural-history book at school or on a calendar put out by an insurance company. People all over the township stared at their calendars in wonderment. Most of them up to this point thought the picture on the calendar was simply the figment of an artist's imagination.

"There's something indecent about the look of the thing," pronounced my mother.

"I know a bit about bears up in northern Michigan where I was in the lumber camp and wolves and the odd lynx, but those things look odd to me. You'd have to use a cannon to get one," added Grandfather.

Business boomed at the Commercial in the back room where spirits were sold in spite of the Canada Temperance Act. Jake and George held forth as experts on moose lore. To add to the romance of the whole thing they were going to Manitoulin Island, which up to this point I always heard was an Indian burying place.

Finally the fateful day arrived, and they set out. Practically every person in Clover was down at the depot to see them on their way. They had rifles issued to the local Government Rifle Club (I think they were called Ross rifles) and enough gear for an army. They were also in what you might modestly call high spirits.

The residents of the village and the township waited expectantly. Jake and George slipped back into the village at night, and next day the word went around that they had shot a moose. At first no one would pay any attention to the rumors, but then people said it was true. It was over the big mirror behind the bar in the back room of the Commercial. There was something strange about it, however. There was only the head and shoulders of the creature tacked to a board. It looked like the calendar pictures, however.

When George was asked about how they shot the moose he always referred them to Jake. It seemed that a municipal official might give more credence to the story. Thus it was that nightly in the back room of the Commercial, Jake would talk while George served. As I understand it, the story went something like this:

"Me and George had been tramping through those woods with this Indian fella for about two days when suddenly we see big moose coming. I took aim and shot, and I missed. Then Jake shot and missed, and the Indian fellow yelled at us to jump aside. That big moose thundered by us like the City Express and he missed us. He turned and you could see the grass and dirt fly for a quarter-mile."

He always paused at this spot and looked to George for a refill, but usually there were at least a dozen offers. He indicated his favor in the acceptance.

"Well," he would say dramatically, "now we really weren't what you might call experienced hunters except for coons or rabbits, and so we have to admit that we didn't have a real chance against that big fellow. You know that moose was bigger than the dray horse at the livery."

Stopping to take a sip made this dramatic!

"Now, what would you do in a situation like that?"

His audience gasped. After a dramatic pause Jake would say, "You have to give George credit for being a quick witted man."

Then George modestly swiped the bar with a rag.

"He pulled a quart of moonshine we had bought from

Sheep Willy before we left and let fly right in the face of the moose."

Again he paused. The audience by this time would be paralyzed. Jake would shake his head as if memory of the moment was too horrifying to be recalled.

"Now," he added solemnly, "George knows the pace of a trotter or a pacer, but he misjudged the moose, and that's understandable."

His audience was in agreement.

"He splashed that moose on the hind quarter in the most tender spots and by the gobs of war what do you think happened? That moose just shook and dug in his hoofs and squatted right down on the bare rock. There's a lot of rock up there. Well, he started rubbing and he rubbed away until all that was left is what you see there."

Then he would point to the tortured face of the moose on the cedar plank over the bar. To this day the moose head is in the Commercial Hotel bar. Any old-timer will tell you the story for the price of a couple of refills, just the way I have. The length of the version will depend on his thirst.

There is probably no time of the year with so strong a lure for the displaced countryman as the fall.

The dipping of the night temperatures makes certain that the paintbrush starts to show up in the early coloring of hardwood trees. Along the field lines, down lanes and where trees stand like sentinels by roadside fences, the maples are blushing.

The remaining wood lots on farms show the splotched effect of the trees that have bowed to the cold and turned full color to contrast with the hardier ones of their own varieties and the evergreens, which seem somehow to have deepened their resistance and remained more stolidly green than ever.

The whole thing demands deep deliberation, recall of precedents and a great deal of conversation. Man is always seeking the reason for the perversity of wind and weather.

The advantage of an early autumn is the fact that the liquid nights, filled with the sounds of crickets, seem to come early. Our fall may even be longer as a compensation for the shortened summer.

We enjoyed those nights to the fullest extent, the family sitting out on the back porch without bothering to light a lamp. There was an occasional spatter of conversation, but most of the time there was a silent enjoyment. It was enough to hear a clatter in the distance as a horse and buggy went over the creek bridge, the sound of a farmer calling his cows to a late milking or the barking of a dog roused for some reason or other, creating a minor mystery for lazy pondering.

"Must be a skunk or something."

"Soon be coon weather."

"That red cow of Ab's must have broken into the orchard agin."

It was dropped without solving and we went on. Hardy hens who had escaped the night roundup could be heard in the wild apple tree in the lane. The birds were restless in the big pines, murmuring and scolding in feathery stumbling on the branches. An early fall always bothered them as if it were crossing up their natural senses. It made the chipmunks and squirrels nervous, as they might not be able to gather their winter supplies in time.

In this time of new fall, there is the wonder and glory of the meeting of dying sun and borning moon. We seem first of all to be suspended in a flat plate with the sky arching in a full half circle, seeming a greater sky than at any time before.

The sun takes a hand and dapples the clouds with

lights that few earthbound artists can ever truly capture. With a lavish hand the sun will splash pinks, golds, reds, bronzes . . . everything in the paint box, as if to shame the puny efforts of frost and nature on the trees. Boiling clouds become hellish caldrons, spilling Niagara riots of soft pinks and golds and then, lavalike, flowing across a whole strip of the sky.

A perfect fall night is spectacular. It never ceases because in the very act of being it is also changing. Dramatically as it shifts, with the sun sinking, the emphasis changes. Now there is backlighting and the trees across the earth are outlined like spidery creations of blackened silver standing against the sky. The weird yellowish-green light comes up over the whole vast bowl of sky with darker effects in the east and the rim of the world seemingly catching on fire.

"Look, the moon."

I suppose that has been a cry since man first gave a name to this pale creature of the night skies.

She seems to be slipping silently into the great amphitheater, waiting for a cue and knowing that the sun is dying and must truly vanish before she can create a magic show of her own.

But there can be no true rivalry between this pair. The sun has a cue sheet in the heavenly drama and must abide by the rules. The moon can flit around with a pale presence because she is merely limbering up and getting into position. Yet, there remains for a time a lingering glow as the sun withdraws and leaves more and more sky territory, suffusing finally only a melancholy strip across the western rim of the earth.

On fall nights when the air has a crisp tanginess that feels like a Spy apple tastes, the stars come winking on. The moon presents her court, hoping it would appear that by reason of sheer numbers and the fantasy of the sight she can rival in grandeur if not in force, the effect of the sun.

On certain fall nights man, forgetting the need for the sun and its energies, might even settle for the sirens of the night. Certainly, no day enlivened by the sun can bring the peace and gentle contentment of the night when moon and attendants fragment the sky with scattered silver.

These days have always been associated in my mind with Indians. There is no apparent reason for this. Perhaps it came from early reading or the fact we used to have Indian families encamped on the river flats in the fall, when they were nudging through the woods looking for roots and herbs such as ginseng root.

Maybe it was the sight of their little fires as we drove by, the thin columns of smoke wavering up to become lost in the air and the sky. Perhaps it was their color which blended so well with the changing color of our world in the fall season.

When I walked beside the river, cutting across the meadows by the swale and striding into the long marsh grass, it was easy to imagine what the place must have been like before the white man intruded. It was fun to try and imagine stalking game through a world which, in my fantasy, I thought must have all been hip-deep in waving grass. I suppose my unprofessional research may have confused Plains Indians with Ontario Indians, and I must admit my imagination also allowed buffalo to romp through our meadows.

There was another joy in the fall. We had a pear tree near the river. This was probably the remains of a very early pioneer homestead, and it was a gnarled and crooked veteran that bore fruit in a haphazard manner. One year it was festooned with an enormous number of pears. Next season it would have only scattered fruits of poor quality.

So there was an element of surprise. The trick was to pick the pears while they were still very firm and keep them away from predators—human and animal.

I tried a haystack, but found that in the ripening process they attracted a lot of customers. Once, my own father appeared with his smock pockets filled with the fruit, exulting that he had found a squirrel store. I tried the driving shed, and the rats or mice got into them. One year I was canny and carefully put a dozen or so away amongst the tissue-covered clothes in our spare bedroom in a bureau that was seldom used.

I forgot about the pears with so much to eat in the way of apples and other fruit, and I only remembered when Mother went to get out her spring suit for Easter Sunday. In all honesty, that's about the only painful memory I have about the golden season of autumn. At that I don't think my punishment would have been half so severe if my guffawing father hadn't suggested that she dye the whole suit in a "squashed pear color."

CHAPTER 9

THE QUIET MEN

Tolerance and understanding didn't happen in our community over night. The progress from pioneer days had been studded with nurtured animosities. There were many barroom fights over what individuals considered to be religious slurs. "Papist" was a fighting word. Similarily, a professed Orangeman walked gently in a barroom around July 12 when he found himself outnumbered by Irish Catholics. The Battle of the Boyne might still stir up a Donnybrook.

Something happened during the Great War of 1914–18. It became apparent that there was no difference in how a Catholic or a Protestant could be maimed or killed. Neither bravery nor cowardice were prerogatives of an individual sect.

The ones who came back were quiet men for the most part. I often think each covered his own personal mystery. They were like the visitor who came to spend an afternoon in the hard spring light of our kitchen. The jerky pasteboard figures of a World War I film make me see and sense him as if once again he were sitting beside me.

He came walking down our concession on a Saturday when the snow was rotting. He seemed to be barely moving so that the tail of his greatcoat stirred gently instead of slapping against his putteed legs. He was very tall, a wrapped-up pole of a man with a soldier's cap squished down over his forehead. He paused in his walking to place his hands on our roadway gate. It seemed as if he didn't have the strength to open it.

"He's coming up the laneway," said Grandfather.

My father stood up and put on his cap and then waited for a little while with his hand on the latch of the kitchen door. He opened it.

"Good day."

The man nodded as if trying to save energy. "I'd be obliged for a drink of water."

He stood inside the door, and his Adam's apple bobbed as he drank the cold water from the pantry pail. It touched off a series of explosive coughs like firecrackers, and as he dropped into the chair I could see tears in his eyes.

"You could stand something to eat," exclaimed Mother, beginning a series of motions that were strangely co-ordinated as she stirred the fire, filled the kettle, set cup, saucer, and plate on the table, and started cutting meat from a cold roast.

He didn't answer. Father examined his hands and Grandfather took a long time filling his pipe. The man produced a pipe, and Grandfather silently handed over his plug. The stranger looked helpless until he was handed a knife. There was something almost greedy in the way he cut at the tobacco, rubbed it in his hand and filled the pipe. He drew on it after lighting it, with short, little puffs. Then he held the bowl in his hand and smiled for the first time, in a way that relaxed the shiny skin from the bony face.

"They don't let us smoke at the hospital."

"Oh?" exclaimed Father in a way that made him look self-conscious because it was so questioning.

The man didn't say anything when Mother pressed him

to take off his greatcoat. He was wearing an old uniform that had ordinary buttons on it and faded spots where the insignia had been taken off. His hair was bristly and gray except for a startling white streak. He ate slowly, taking minute bites and washing each one down with tea.

"That's good tea, ma'am."

Mother smiled and filled the cup again. He drank the tea as if trying to absorb the warmth. In the quiet of the kitchen the usual noises seemed loud. The clock, the patterned groaning of the floor boards under the rocker, and the sleeping groans from Snap behind the stove occupied us in place of conversation.

Finally, Father said, "Are you going far?"

The man stirred and looked at him as if he had been thinking thoughts so far away it was hard to get back into the present.

"The Carpenters . . . do they still live on the side road?"

Father, Mother, Grandfather and myself looked at each other. There was that air of sadness about the stranger that made you realize that bad news had ceased to have any effect on him.

"They both died last winter."

He nodded as if he had been expecting it. He didn't say anything.

"Did you know . . . .I mean are you kin to the Carpenters?"

He shook his head. "I was a home boy, and I spent two summers there."

My grownups looked shocked. It was Grandfather who said, "You'd be Jack Straw."

The man looked as if only his lips and chin were smiling, or perhaps I couldn't tell because his eyes were sunk so deep in the sockets you could hardly see them.

"Jack Sarton . . . Mr. Carpenter called me Straw."

There was a rush of conversation then as my folks explained the deaths of the Carpenters, one following the other by only a day with the flu.

"Mr. Carpenter was very good to me. Remember how he used to drive me to Mass every Sunday."

The folks nodded.

"He did that in spite of his bitterness over his daughter being a convert."

"A fair man," said my father, as the others nodded.

The conversation dribbled on, and presently he stood up and put on his greatcoat. When he wouldn't let Father hitch up and drive him to look at the Carpenter place, Mother pressed a package of food on him, which he tucked in the big pockets.

He went off down the concession slowly, and I went to the parlor and spent the time in looking up the big *Illustrated History of the 1914–18 War* that Father had bought from a peddler. It seemed to come very close to me. Later on, I saw him barely moving as he walked back and he stopped at the gateway. I hoped he would come in so I might ask him about the pictures. It would be easier to talk to him on the second visit. Father was just going to ask him in when he walked on. Next day my father made an excuse to go to the village. Mr. Black, the station agent, said the man had taken the train back to the city.

We never saw him or heard of him again, and yet there are times when I can see him as plainly as I did on that afternoon in our kitchen on the farm.

People also remember what the war did to Red Dan McKenzie. He was a tall, gaunt man with a brush of wiry gray hair and a red face that looked as if it were bleeding from being freshly carved. His shoulders were broad. For some reason or other I always thought he looked like a tree. In spite of being old he seemed ageless, and he walked and stood like a part of the very ground beneath him.

Red Dan was a good farmer who lived in Maple township, just over the boundary line from Clover. He was an ardent Presbyterian who gave the impression that most of the people in our valley were on the high road to hell for scandalous living. He fought against the installation of an organ in the church saying that it was nothing but a "kist of whustles." He thought his cousin Red Sandy was an instrument of the devil because he played a violin.

To most of the neighbors, Red Dan seemed like an old Highland chieftain. They used to smile at my uncle's store when the McKenzies came to buy. Incidentally the only reason they bought from my uncle was because the old man thought the village life in Clover was "vurry fast" and he didn't want his daughter and two sons to be unduly influenced.

Mrs. McKenzie was a shy creature who looked at the ground if she happened to meet anyone, and when they spoke she would look up quickly and reply and then move along like a frightened deer. The family consisted of Alex and Tom and a daughter Flora. They had each been removed from school when they passed their entrance examinations and put to work.

When the group came shopping the old man would stand beside the big stove and wait while Mrs. McKenzie and Flora did the actual buying. My uncle said Mrs. McKenzie used to whisper the order to him as if she didn't want her husband to hear. The two boys waited outside in summertime or else came in and pretended to be examining the overall counter. When Mrs. McKenzie finished shopping Red Dan would step up and examine the bill as prepared by my uncle.

"Air ye sure ye need it all?" was the invariable question,

and Mrs. McKenzie would bob her head and blush. The old man would take out his purse and pay.

The McKenzies went to church three times each Sunday and to prayer meeting on Wednesdays. They were not allowed to play cards or go to dances, and when they came to a garden party they didn't play any games like Wheel of Fortune or Acey-Deucy. They ate as much as possible and went home before the entertainment. A hired man once said he had worked for Red Dan one summer and that the old man read every evening from the Bible until the light was too poor, and then everyone was expected to go to bed.

It was agreed in the community the old man was a stern parent and a taskmaster to work for, but no one said anything. It was his home and his family and while there could be a great deal of gossip about it, I suspect that he was forgiven a lot because he was such a competent farmer. He had two hundred acres of good bottomland and the best barn in the valley. It was said that he didn't have a thistle on the place. That's no wonder because he worked the whole family at pulling weeds when there wasn't other work to do.

The McKenzie house was a small log one covered with clapboard built by his pioneer father. When other farmers in the time before the war were building large brick and stone houses he was adding more land and more buildings such as pigpen and a driving shed.

There were quite a number of older men who seemed stern. They would at least speak to a youngster or a woman and even smile. That wasn't the case with Red Dan. He drove in to our place on Saturday, and when he stopped the horse at the stoop of the back porch, he growled at Mother, "Tell your husband that Mistair McKenzie is here to see him about buying some lambs." Mother scurried off without saying anything. She said later she was either too mad or too frightened to say anything.

Red Dan was opposed to the war. Departing from his usual practice of not commenting on anything except the lack of religious fervor in the district, he was quite vocal about the war.

"It's none of our business. My sons won't go to war."

The story is that when Alex was called up Red Dan drove to see the authorities in Handrich claiming exemption because many farmers' sons were given this for being essential workers. When he came home with the exemption, Alex had enlisted on his own. The war was just the opportunity the young man had been waiting for, to escape from the old man.

It is still said in our community that Red Dan never mentioned Alex's name again, at least to anyone outside of his family. In 1916 Alex was killed. Red Dan forbade the minister of the kirk to say prayers for him. Something happened, which the neighbors could only guess at, but Tom, the younger son, went to Camp Borden, where they were forming a flying school, and he ended up in the Royal Flying Corps, later the Royal Canadian Air Force.

This was exciting news in our community, and everyone was buzzing with it, but Red Dan seemed to grow more silent and uncommunicative than ever. Tom came home after the war wearing a flyer's uniform. He was the only airman from Clover, and the girls were swooning at the depot when he arrived, much to the disgust of the other veterans.

Tom had changed, however.

He spent a good deal of time at my uncle's store. He seemed to be restless and unhappy.

"It was natural," my father often said, "for a fellow like Tom to find it hard to go back to that life. Red Dan had been hard put to keep up during the war and he started in

when Tom came back as if he wanted to make up for all
the lost time."

Tom started smoking cigarettes and complained bitterly
to the neighbors that his father forbade him smoking
around the farm. Tom refused to go to church, and the old
man kept trying to bully him. The only evident sign of
weakness that Red Dan displayed was when he stood up at
prayer meeting and asked his fellow parishioners to help
him pray and wrest his son's soul back from the devil.

When Tom heard about it he walked all the way into
Clover and, meeting some of his wartime friends, proceeded to the back room of the Commercial Hotel. News
of drinking bouts was not just automatically relayed to
someone of my age, so I had to glean what I could out of
various conversations. Tom evidently didn't go home but
slept overnight at the Smoke Hole, a nook at the back of
Olsen's Blacksmith Shop.

During the next afternoon the party was resumed at the
Commercial, and someone must have told Red Dan because the old man appeared and ordered Tom home. The
air was so thick with tension that George Warner stepped
out from behind the bar and nodded to Olsen, a big brawny
man, to help him. Tom didn't argue but shrugged his
shoulders and went home in the buggy with his father. It
shocked everybody and they agreed the old man had won.
They expected Tom to settle back in the routine.

They hadn't realized how much difference the war had
made. Tom was seen walking down the road with a knap-
sack over his back two days later. Mr. Black at the station
said he had gone to Handrich, the county town. Later it
turned out he went to Detroit and was working for Henry
Ford at fabulous wages.

People didn't like to mention it to Red Dan, but my
uncle said a commercial traveler was in the general store

one day and struck up a rather one-sided conversation with Mr. McKenzie while Mrs. McKenzie and Flora were shopping.

"Ah, the war was a terrible thing," said the traveler, "I lost a son at Ypres. Did you have any sons in the war, sir?"

Mrs. McKenzie, Flora, and my uncle waited with drawn breaths for the answer, and the old man said finally and dryly, "I lost two . . . one to the Huns and one to the Yankies."

The drummer wisely didn't say any more.

CHAPTER 10

THE MARRYING KIND

We had a war bride after the '14–'18 war. She was an unusual woman who came into a set of circumstances that would have smothered any ordinary person. Her name was Leela and she was born in London. She was the first Cockney that most people in the community had ever heard, and she married Albert Jenks.

He was a son of Sheep Willy, the chieftain of the shiftless and yet colorful group that lived in a form of grand squalor near the village dump by a meandering creek. I suppose every community has a Jenks family. Ours was the despair and envy of a lot of people for a carefree existence.

Sheep Willy worked once a year in sheep-shearing time. He excelled at this job. It was a sight to behold him stripped to the waist rolling a fleece off with hand clippers, pausing only now and again to eradicate some of the ticks which had transferred allegiance from the sheep to his matted chest, or to wipe his brow with his forearm and take a swig of what he called his "asthma" medicine from a stone jug.

This was homebrew of a particularly violent nature, which he could be induced to sell now and again to thirsty patrons whom he trusted.

The Jenks brood worked fitfully, when and if money was needed for such things as getting shoes for the children in the fall or buying Christmas presents. They trapped muskrats on the creek in the spring, dug out fox dens, poached trout from the Clover Fish and Game Society preserve, stole bee trees in the dark of night. It was suspected they might have been a contributing factor in the loss of turkeys and geese to predatory influences around Thanksgiving time.

They were usually happy, clannish in spite of frequent family squabbles. Dr. Jamieson said they were the healthiest bunch in three townships. Their home was a weird assortment of rooms, added as families were added, and it was known locally as "the Castle."

This bothered Mrs. Henderson, wife of the banker, who had spent a great deal of money building a home of startling proportions on a hill overlooking the village which she said copied the plans of her ancestral home in Scotland. It was called locally "the Croft," but never to her face.

Albert was the youngest of the Jenks boys when war broke out, and in a way he was somehow different from the others. He was inclined to be bookish, worked fairly steadily at Murphy's Emporium and occasionally responded to invitations by Reverend McPherson in attending the Presbyterian church.

He enlisted and went away without any fuss, although Sheep Willy was broken up and went to bed with his "asthma" and his jug of medicine. Late at night, people passing over the river bridge recalled hearing him singing in a loud voice some cowboy laments.

Sheep Willy was not, at first, what you call a patriot, and he forbade his other sons to enlist. They promptly joined up. Then Sheep Willy became a patriot and flew a large Union Jack over the castle. He gathered salvage with a great determination. In fact he became the biggest single contributor by simply cleaning up the front yard of the Castle, which had been full of junk.

The Jenkses were good soldiers and sailors. One was in the air service. One was killed.

When two came home, Albert didn't show up. He had married a girl in London and had evidently set out to work in England. He was forgotten by the community but not by Sheep Willy.

"That lad will be home," he kept saying, "he's a Canadian and he loves his family. That's the way with us. We're a real family, and he'll be back."

He was a true prophet, because Mr. Black, the station agent, leaked word that Albert had wired in the spring of 1920 saying he was coming home with his bride.

That set off a real split in the community.

Some said that Albert had always been different from the rest of the Jenks family and would never be content. Others said that blood will tell. Still others posed the question of the bride, suggesting that Cockney was something like a tribe and that she would never put up with that kind of living afforded in the Castle.

It was amazing how many people found reasons to be at the station on that summer morning when Albert and his wife arrived. The reports were varied about the reception committee of the Jenks family, but it must have been quite a scene.

Sheep Willy drove them back in style, while the rest of the family walked behind. Their new home was a railroad boxcar which had been sold as salvage and dragged by the family and put at right angles to the rest of the Jenks home.

It had been decorated with a sign, "Bridal Suite," furnished with furniture donated by the other families, and was considered quite elaborate because a window had been installed, although the sliding doors remained on the front. There was, of course, running water in the creek.

Leela was a brave girl. She overlooked the welcoming party, which was said to have lasted for a week, or until they ran out of bootleg whiskey. She put curtains on the window of the boxcar wing, scratched out a garden, and had flower pots along a small, graveled walk.

The battle came over church and work. Leela liked the fundamentalist note of the red-brick Methodist church. Sheep Willy said he was an atheist and he didn't want any of his boys going to church.

Leela wanted Albert to go to work. She wanted a steady income. The Jenks clan didn't believe in work. Sheep Willy was a strong man who didn't work.

The news ran through Clover like a grassfire that Albert's wife was working at the Commercial Hotel. Not only that, she was living at the hotel.

Albert started coming to sit on the front veranda of the hotel. Leela ignored him. This went on for a month, and one day Albert started helping in the livery stable. Leela still was not convinced that wasn't a trick.

Then Albert went to work regularly as a clerk at Murphy's Emporium, but it was not until he had bought a new suit of clothes from Jimmy Medd and rented a small house behind the Presbyterian church that Leela consented to go back with him.

One night when Leela was working, Sheep Willy and two of his boys went to visit Albert. They wanted to be friendly and brought along a jug of homebrew.

Leela heard the singing when she turned the corner by the church, and she must have really been angry. She took a broom and chased the three of them all the way to Main Street. When she got back, Albert had to make his final choice. He stayed, and Leela was given full marks by everyone.

William Jenks, the grandson, was christened the following spring, and they say Sheep Willy was a model of sartorial splendor when he attended at the red-brick Methodist church.

It was considered another mark of quality in Leela when she invited him to the christening. War brides, after that, were given high marks in our district.

When Mother heard "Red Joe" Wilson was going to marry Jeanie Laidlaw, she was horrified. She liked both of them, but the thought of the untidy bachelor married to the dust-chasing hired girl didn't seem reasonable. Red Joe lived on fifty acres on the river side road in comfortable squalor induced by twenty-odd years of bachelorhood. Jeanie had come from Scotland to find her boyfriend of the '14-'18 war had succumbed to the lure of a former schoolmate who had the extra attraction of inheriting a one-hundred-acre farm. Jeanie went to work, a scrubbed atom of energy, who whacked dirt and dust as if they reminded her of the former suitor.

"It can't be true," declared Mother after hearing about the wedding banns, "that big lunk married to that little wisp of movement."

Grandfather chuckled.

"Well, it's the only place in the township she hasn't cleaned up."

That amused us. Jeanie had been at our place for a month when Mother had pneumonia, and she worked and cleaned and scrubbed to the point where the invalid got well in self-defense. She was afraid the neighbors would think her house had been untidy before Jeanie came.

The marriage of Red Joe and Jeanie interested my

mother in an almost passionate way. She fussed and fretted about it.

"I wonder if that poor girl has any idea of what she is getting into?"

"No right-minded person would move into a den of filth like that."

You could see it was troubling her. Mind you, Red Joe was an itinerant attendant at the white-brick Methodist church, and custom decreed that someone in the congregation should take a hand. It was another of the unwritten rules.

Father didn't help by saying, "Young love is blind."

Mother snorted. "You silly, old ass. Red Joe is older than I am, and Jeanie is no chicken either."

Father retreated behind the newspaper but Grandfather, for once, put his foot in it. "Well, what can you or anybody else do about it?"

"I'll tell you," said Mother, her chin firming, "we are going to be good neighbors and clean up the mess for Jeanie. It's the charitable thing to do."

Father came up from behind his defense line.

"You mean," he said, with his Adam's apple bobbing, "you mean, we just announce to Red we're going to clean up his place."

Mother nodded, her hand reaching for a stub of pencil and an old calendar pad which she used to write notes on. "We are going to be good neighbors, and religion doesn't matter." She wrote something and added, "For Jeanie. She likes things clean and it's only fair to do this."

Father muttered his doubts, but I was old enough to bank on Mother. It sounded like fun to me. On the Saturday before the wedding, Grandfather tried to play "cramps." He always had cramps when there was something to do he didn't like, but Mother nudged him onto the bobsleigh with Father and myself. We drove back the lane-way, let down the line fence, and went along the river bank.

"What the neighbors don't know," announced Mother, "won't hurt them."

Joe was a man with a barrel body and legs that seemed too small to support him. He had a big, round face that flushed red like a sign under the customary rime of faded red beard. He had a forelock of hair standing up like a fiery horn and looked startling in contrast with the polished spot of bald behind it. His overalls were constantly stiff with an accumulation of chop, oil, grease, and what was probably remnants of meals. Buttons were never replaced, and he substituted arrangements of looped twine or string and bits of wire. He shuffled in his boots and blushed when we came into the yard.

"Awful good of you folks to come over. I cleaned up pretty good, but I suppose it needs a woman to final polish it."

His kitchen, normally a nightmare of smoky, torn wall-paper, piles of old newspapers, tin cans, empty bottles, dirty dishes, broken harnesses, partially whittled neck yokes, and bones the dogs worried at, was now fairly orderly. Ashes still dripped from the stove and the floor looked black from dirt and grease, but a lot of the clutter was gone. Grandfather was all for going home but Mother soon found the answer. Red Joe had shoveled all the truck into a spare room and closed the door.

"Joe, you're the limit. What did you expect your bride to do with this?"

He stammered. "Didn't know where to put it and so I just . . . sort of . . . well . . . put it out of the way."

Mother took over. She was a working and commanding general, and we were ordinary slogging soldiers. The front yard blazed with a fire, and the other truck was taken back and dumped into an old, used gravel pit. Water bubbled and boiled in the kettles and was applied with liberal quantities of strong soap. It took two days, and Grandfather and Joe, who had a habit of trying to vanish into the barn, were always rounded up.

The walls were stripped of paper. The floor was scrubbed to a bleached gray showing the grain. Windows that were broken and stuffed with rags and papers were replaced. We relaxed, thinking that was the end, but Mother had other plans. My uncle, who ran the general store, drove in with a load of wallpaper, paint, and what he called a "congoleon" rug of linoleum. It all was applied as well, and when Joe muttered about cost, Mother withered him.

"Shame on you. You're getting a fine girl." She added practically, "A saving one, too, who probably has a tidy bit from her work."

The place looked wonderful, and Mother added curtains for the kitchen. She told Joe in no uncertain terms about keeping the dogs out, and we left with him sitting in stunned silence on a rocker brought from the attic, gingerly rocking on the shiny linoleum rug.

On the morning of the wedding he arrived at our place, stiff as a window dummy in a blue suit and boiled collar. Mother, who hadn't started getting ready, stopped on the way upstairs and came back to stare at the big man with something like shock on her face.

"Joe, there's no time for niceness now. Did you take a bath?"

For a time it looked as if he would either swallow his tongue or his face would explode. He shook his head. Father and Grandfather tried to get out the kitchen door but she blocked them. Mother was in deadly earnest. She faced Red Joe and started to say, "Now look, this is none of my affair, but somebody has to find out before it's too late. Did you . . ."

She stopped and looked a trifle flustered and then bored on as if the need was greater than her natural modesty. "Did you get new underwear?"

The big man shook his head miserably.

Mother went into action, and so it came to pass that a sheepish Father and Grandfather bathed Red Joe in the chilly back woodshed and shoehorned him into the new sets of ganseys which Mother had given Father for Christmas. They were small for the bridegroom, and we got to church just in time. The wedding went well. Joe and Jeanie took an overnight train trip to Guelph, combining business with pleasure, because Joe went to buy a purebred ram at the agricultural college. Jeanie was a Highlander, and she insisted on Joe starting a herd of sheep. Father agreed to do the overnight chores.

"Well," announced Mother, as we were driving home, "he was clean, skin and all, and so was his house. Jeanie can't say anything about the neighbors."

I wondered then if her charity hadn't been tinged a bit with revenge for the four weeks of cleaning at our house. Father started to laugh, however.

"I wonder how he'll ever get out of that set of combinations?"

Grandfather capped it by saying, "Take a Scotch girl to understand a tight situation like that."

Sound carried on the frosty air and people on the next concession heard us and ribbed Father about drinking too much at the wedding. That wasn't true. It was dry, because Jeanie was Temperance Union as well as Methodist.

CHAPTER 11
CHRISTMAS AT THE LEES'

Perhaps at no time in the year were Catholics and Methodists more united than at Christmastime. No spirit of ecumenism could have projected any greater measure of tolerance than that afforded by this season.

There was a Christmas concert in the Catholic church basement with entertainment provided by the pupils of the separate school. Under the big tree there were presents being exchanged by the children, but there was also a large box filled with individual bags containing hard candies, creams, nuts, and an orange. Every child in attendance received one of these. Because it was our night to shine, we dominated the event. Father Morrison was chairman and repeated several stories from the year before and provoked gales of laughter.

On another evening during the Christmas season there was a concert at the white-brick Methodist church. The public school pupils exchanged gifts and provided the concert. They exchanged gifts, but each child present received a package with hard candies, creams, nuts, and an orange. It was their night to shine and dominate the event. Reverend McPherson was chairman and he told stories we had heard before and they provoked gales of laughter.

Santa Claus was amazingly similar. At least his costume was the same, because there was a tear on the knee. Years later I learned that my uncle was our Santa Claus and Mr. Higgins was the Methodist one, but my uncle owned the suit.

The Christmas tree was in many ways the focal point of the whole family spirit of the season.

It meant that the rarely used front room would glow with warmth and color. It was also the place for the Christmas gifts. But, in addition, there was something magnificent about bringing a part of the outside scenery inside and making it a part of the festivities.

Whether we recognized it or not, we were very closely related to nature and perhaps this green handiwork of Mother Nature symbolized more than we realized. However, symbolism aside, there was the practical matter of getting the tree.

The decision was usually made at the supper table after the first hard fall of snow.

Both Father and Grandfather always thought it was much too early in the season to cut a Christmas tree. It would dry out and the needles would shower from it. There was a certain time to cut a tree when it was best. They couldn't explain it when Mother pressed them, but they somehow thought there was a certain time. That night coming home from school I would fairly race to see if the tree had been cut. There was no sign of it, and I went in to supper with a long face.

Halfway through supper Grandfather would be moved by my obvious hurt and say, "Mighty good tree we got."

Mother's instinctive reaction was to say, "Finish your supper."

"Where is it?"

"You can see it after supper," was the reply.

The food would be splashed and shoveled in, and finally Grandfather took me out behind the woodshed to where the monster stood. It was usually festooned with snow, having been dragged from the back fifty. But there it stood, dark green and mighty!

The tree came in by degrees. First of all, it was squeezed in through the doors of the woodshed, and shoved into the back kitchen where the snow melted from it. Next it was compressed as tightly as possible, and we began the dangerous task of trying to get it in through the kitchen and into the parlor without swushing things in all directions.

A large Christmas tree is something to be reckoned with in the confines of a kitchen. Father pulled at the base while Grandfather and I tried to smother the twiggy limbs. Mother fluttered by, grabbing pots and pans from the stove and dishes from the sideboard as the monster progressed.

"Take it easy," counseled Mother.

"What do you think I'm doing," growled Father, as he gave the trunk a vicious pull. Grandfather lurched and let a large limb flip up dangerously close to the clock.

"Couldn't you have tied it?" Mother would demand.

"We'll get it in," was Father's stock reply as he slammed it the other way and my limb took the oilcloth off the kitchen table.

The real test was yet to come—in the parlor. Mother, seeing that the tree was coming like an avenger, would sweep ahead of it, gathering up everything from ornamental gewgaws to the samplers from the walls and the candles from the holders on the ends of the organ.

The small table with the crossed legs that held the family pictures was invariably skeltered over, but the tree would be propped up in the corner across from the cast-iron heater, and Father would get the saw. This Mother dreaded more than anything. There was something profane about hammering and sawing in that varnished sanctuary.

It was worth it, however, to see the tree standing tall, dark, and straight. Even without the fire on, the room began to smell of that wild and oily essence of cedar.

At night, before going to bed, I would sneak into the frosty room and stand in the presence of the dark creature. Then I'd go back to bed and dream of the day when it would come alive as a part of our Christmas.

The decorations seemed wonderful in those days! We didn't have any plastic cedar cones or things like that. There were some glass balls that glittered with all the colors of the rainbow, real cedar cones with red ribbons, angels made from cotton fluff with tinsel wings, accordionlike tissue balls of red and green, garlands of some kind of red and green rope, and odds and ends of ordinary things like saved scraps of colored paper, twisted into bells or balls. Silvery paper was cut into strips and made into quite realistic icicles. When everything else failed, there were cutouts of churches and houses from old Christmas cards.

Then the candles were put in place. A modern fire commissioner mustn't read this. These were small snap-on holders for tiny, spiraled wax candles, but they were not lit until Christmas Eve.

Of course there were other things added to the tree as the days went by. At school we made crayon drawings which might qualify in modern art as abstract, but which dutifully were taken home and poked in amongst the branches. The fire was put on every evening during the week before Christmas, and it was a delight beyond words to watch the gilded giant by the flickering light from the mica front of the stove.

On Christmas Eve, I could hardly breathe and lingered while putting my stocking in umpteen different places, afraid Santa Claus might miss it. Finally I'd go reluctantly up the cold, bare front stairs that, on this night, didn't even seem cold.

In bed I tried to stay awake by thinking of the tree and the shining star. With the joyful, ringing sound of childish hope in my heart, I would sift into sleep.

Christmas changed in our village during the past years. Many people in Clover and from the township now complain that the season has been gaudied up. They have decorations from the lampposts along Main Street and an arch in front of the township hall with a Merry Christmas banner. At night two speakers in front of the hardware store spill out electronic Christmas carols. If we have a snowstorm before Christmas, the whole scene has real atmosphere, especially if it's the fluffy kind of snow that blankets everything and piles up on the big spruce trees in front of the United church.

If you happen to be in our village on Christmas Day be sure to visit Lee's Café. Billy and Jenny Lee give out free meals that day. Most people, of course, want to eat at home on a day like Christmas, but practically everybody drops in for coffee or tea, and they get a kick out of having fortune cookies. The restaurant will be all fixed up with wreaths and bells, and there will be a big cake on the counter. You're expected to have something, and Billy, who is a bit on the fat side, will "shuffer" out in those slippers that always seem too big for him, and this year he'll explain that in the Chinese way 1965 is the year of the Snake.

The two girls, Emmy and Jill, will be there. Emmy comes home from college. Jill goes to the new consolidated high school. Chris may even get home from the city. I hope he does, because he is really the reason for open house at Lee's Café on Christmas Day. A lot of the young people won't know what the celebration is about, but the older folk remember and appreciate this recognition of a Christian holiday by the Chinese couple.

The reason goes back thirty-five years to a Christmas Eve when we were all caught in an economic recession and what you might call a bankruptcy of spirit. Hard times crept up on us instead of striking swiftly as it had done in the city. It was almost impossible to sell anything, and the scarcity of money was acute. The fact that we had plenty to eat cushioned the rural community from the hard impact of the depression in the city.

"This is going to be a mighty slim Christmas," Mother kept saying, as she stared at the unattainable items in the mail-order catalogue.

"If I just had a little ready cash," Father said grumpily, when he returned from trying to sell a load of wood in the village and had to finally swap it for staples at the store.

"I seem to have lost my taste for tobacco," Grandfather said, when I noticed he was scarcely ever smoking, unlike former times, when he scarcely ever took the pipe out of his mouth except to sleep or eat.

In the village I found I had a yearning for oranges, but they were a luxury. At that, I was lucky because I had eighty cents. That was saved up from the two dollars I made helping the roadmaster tally his sheets, used when farmers did road work as part payment on their taxes. Janese, the road superintendent, hadn't much of a head for figures. Actually, he held the job because he was a brother-in-law of the reeve.

I picked a handkerchief for Mother. It had a lot of lace on it and two small colored flowers in the corner. For Dad I bought a very large bottle of shaving lotion. I knew he liked lotion after shaving, but he hadn't had any for a long time. I must confess I hadn't quite figured on the high potency of the stuff in the fancy bottle. With the thirty cents left I paid for a plug of smoking tobacco for Grandfather, a ten-cent bottle of perfume that seemed dainty because it was in such a small bottle, and a nickel's worth of jawbreakers for myself.

In a sense it was a strange Christmas. I knew Father had bought Mother a large box of chocolates. He said when he was buying it, "I know I got a store bill, Joe, but doggone it, I can tell by the look in my wife's eyes when she's staring at the mail-order catalogue that she's just hankering for something she doesn't need." Joe Murphy, the storekeeper, nodded and handed over the candy. "You're right," he said, "my wife said she wanted some stuffed olives for Christmas dinner and some of those marshineye chocolates." They both laughed and in a way, I guess, I sensed what they were talking about.

I knew Mother had knitted a sweater for Father. She traded wool at the Benmiller Woollen Mill for yarn. I was getting a sled that Grandfather made because I saw it up on a joist in the driving shed partly covered up with gunny sacks. We had just settled in to enjoy Christmas Eve when the telephone started ringing strangely. Mother went to listen. She came back shaking her head.

"Something's funny. People talking about Chinamen."

Grandfather said, a trifle wistfully: "Some people must still be able to afford to celebrate."

Then our number rang on the party line. Two longs and three shorts! Father went this time as if he didn't trust Mother. When he came back he was grinning. "Well, it's strange, all right. That was Doc Jamieson's housekeeper. Said a foreign woman's having a baby and wants some warm clothes."

At first they were going to leave me with Grandfather, but I guess we looked so downcast that they took pity on us. I was glad we went because you should have seen that village. That was real Christmas decorating, because the snow was sifting down like a gentle blizzard of goose feathers and the lights were twinkling through.

Our village usually seemed lifeless during the winter, but not on this Christmas Eve. People were standing around on the street and they were shoveling snow and calling out to each other, and all you had to do was follow the line of the crowd right down to the red-brick Methodist church. The lights were all on in the Catholic church hall. A man said if we had clothes to take them in there, and you should have seen the pile of stuff the women were sorting.

Grownups can be terribly maddening at a time like that. I couldn't figure out anything, but the women were all trying to get a little, yellow-faced man to drink tea, and he was trying to avoid being drowned in the stuff. Dr. Jamieson came in. He caught sight of the pile of clothes and said: "Good Lord, I said some baby things." Then he went over and shook hands with the little man and said: "You've got a fine son." That's when I found out that this was a Chinaman, and don't trust that one about Chinese never crying. He just about broke himself in two, and at times you couldn't really tell whether he was crying or laughing.

That's when I learned that people can form mobs for either good or bad things. Dr. Jamieson proposed something about a store on Main Street that he owned and couldn't rent. Everybody trailed over to the place next to the harness maker's. Christmas Eve and all, the women started to clean the place up. A box stove appeared as if by magic, and Father beckoned me to come with him. He was on his way to get an old spool bed from over the back kitchen. While we were slewing around in the snow on the way home he told me about the affair.

"You see, a Chinese fellow and his wife came into the village this afternoon. They were on their way to some other town where his cousin runs a laundry. I guess they hadn't figured on it being so far, and they ran out of gasoline for their old car. They pulled into the Methodist church shed, and he went trying to get some and not a soul would help them . . . being foreign and all. Then, when he went back to the car, he found his wife was having a baby. The Methodist minister went out to see what was happening, and he high-tailed it for Dr. Jamieson. Well, you know the old doctor. He moved the woman into the rectory, and told his housekeeper to tell the people in the district to get busy and help those folks."

He started to chuckle then.

"Never seen a Chinese baby before. They look like us when we're born."

When we stopped the horse and cutter he looked up at the sky and said: "You can almost hear angels tonight."

It was unusual to hear him say anything like that, so he added quickly: "Road's getting heavy. I guess we'll take the team and sleigh on the way back."

I think he felt it was a night for a sleigh ride.

I fell asleep in the sleigh box on the way back. I don't remember too much about that night, but when we left, the old store looked mighty good.

Of course, the Chinese woman and the baby were still at the manse. Next morning at church the whole village, Catholics and Protestants alike, were up and stirring around, taking stuff into the old store. We had a wonderful Christmas, although the shaving lotion got spilled and Grandfather said the stuff smelled like sheep dip. Then, when he got my present, he was sorry he said it, but the sleigh was nice and it was painted red and blue. I got a pair of mittens, an orange, a pencil box with a ruler, and a pencil and a top.

That's about all there is to tell. Billy and Jenny Lee stayed on and opened a café and a candy store. It was very hard going at first, but they made out, and that's why they show their appreciation every Christmas Day. They're proud of the two girls, Emmy and Jill, but they beam when they talk about the boy who was almost born in the old car in the Methodist church shed. They call him Chris, and I suppose that is short for Christmas. Everybody in our district is proud of Chris Lee. He was the first one from our district to become a professor, and he teaches at the university.

The year I made up my mind Santa Claus was only going to give me useful presents of mittens and scarves and a small treat like a book or a jackknife, he completely surprised me.

On Christmas morning, in place of the small wooden sleigh I had seen Grandfather working on, there was a toboggan.

Snow was lean that year and the Big Hill, being sandy and exposed to the sun had scarcely any sliding surface.

I went to bed each night after scanning the skies for any sign of snow and praying for a real blizzard. Perversely, the elements would sprinkle a little snow and then blow it into fence drifts or the hollows of the fields.

It was beginning to look hopeless. I could sit in the kitchen and look out to where the toboggan leaned against the house in the lee of the veranda. It was varnished and new-looking. Pushing it around the yard was frustrating. This long, sleek affair was made for the big slopes and long runs.

It looked as if I might have to go back to school after the New Year without having had a real outing on the toboggan. Then, on the Saturday before the New Year, the morning was overcast. The world seemed poised and waiting for

something. Big snowflakes ruptured from the clouds and
floated down to earth. They were melting as fast as they
arrived, but the tempo increased and the bare spots soon
had a thin coating of white. Mother had a time restraining
me from pushing out to the hill.

The world was a creation of cotton batting by next morning. The teams on the sleigh made a convoy on the way to
church. Everyone was sharing in that hearty friendliness
that comes when nature has a transformation. Church was
secondary in my thoughts to the anticipation of tobaggan-
ing, and when we got home I had to be almost forcibly re-
strained from going to the hill without anything to eat.

I was swallowing cake as I wallowed through the deep
snow to the top of the hill. The toboggan was a delight. On
the first run the snow flared out on each side with a great
white spume effect. A touch of morning breeze had blown
snow off the pond so that when we hit the ice the momen-
tum carried the toboggan part way up the low hill opposite.

Snap, my old collie, was suspicious of getting on the toboggan at first, but he soon tired of romping through the
deep snow and then having to wade back to the top. First
time down he jumped halfway and landed head over heels
in the snowbank. Next time he crouched and made the
journey.

It had seemed all week that if the snow came my wildest
dreams of play and happiness would come true. Yet, somehow I grew tired of being alone.

Grandfather was the first to wander over to the hill. He
stamped around a bit and hedged about going down the
hill for a ride. Sensing my mood, he got on, neglecting to
take the pipe out of his mouth. He made a wild swipe for
it about halfway down and left a foot dragging that sent
both of us sprawling into the snow, while the conveyance
went wildly to the bottom.

Father, at the stable door, yelled for us to stay where we were. He retrieved the toboggan and climbed the hill. "Takes some knack to handle one of these things," he suggested to Grandfather.

"You think you're so smart . . . then try it," retorted the older man.

"Well, I don't know what you're crowing about."

"Go on . . . just try it."

Father got on, adjusted his hands to the ropes, and nodded for a push. He sailed down gracefully, getting an extra boost where the hill bulged a bit, and flashed down to the pond. Lifting both hands in triumph as it came to the ice he flipped off as the toboggan went sideways and hit a clump of grass frozen and protruding above the surface.

Grandfather laughed so hard Mother looked out from the kitchen. Soon, in fact before Father had trudged up the hill, she came out to investigate, wearing his overcoat and an old stocking cap. "Are you children having a good time?"

Father lurched to grab her. "Come on, see for yourself what it's like."

Grandfather gave them both a push, and they lost their balance and went sprawling on the toboggan. Down the hill they went but when they reached the bump, both rolled into the snow.

By the time Mother and Father came up, our neighbors Ed Higgins and his wife, driving along the concession in a horse and cutter, swung in the laneway.

"Do you see what you've done," exclaimed Mother in mock anger. "They thought you were killing me."

It developed they were just curious about the toboggan, and it took practically no coaxing to get both of them on the ride. I half expected to go along, but Mother shook her head. Then Father dared Ed to go down the hill standing up, and he did, keeping his balance almost to the pond.

After that Father tried it and flipped at the bump. Mother and Mrs. Higgins got on and went down, taking ages to bring the toboggan back.

I finally got a chance to go down by myself, but when I looked up they had all gone. I trudged back up the hill, half hoping someone might come back to play with me. No one appeared, and when I went to the house Grandfather was asleep on the sofa in the kitchen, Mother was on the couch in the front room, and Father had gone up to bed for a rest.

I kept looking at the models of toboggans in the catalogue until I fell asleep in the old chair. Mother woke me up with the noise as she started to get supper.

"Didn't you have a wonderful time with your toboggan?" she said.

I didn't answer her, and she was so busy she didn't notice. What was there to say?

Calendar fever was a disease that affected most of the population in the country. It started just before Christmas.

The desire to acquire calendars was almost a form of lust, while the actual possession of unlimited numbers and varieties of them was considered in that day and age a form of status symbol. Of course there was also the matter of usefulness.

One thing for certain, a person who hadn't acquired an assortment of calendars by January 1 was either a bit queer or lazy. Sickness wasn't an excuse. There were plenty of people just itching to act as deputies.

There was a vicarious thrill in being able after picking up a calendar for yourself to say, "By the way, Joe asked me to get one for him. He's laid up with lumbago."

When we went to Clover on a certain Saturday, after

either Father or Mother had announced, "We better get a
few calendars before they're all gone," it was a game.

In fact, it was like a sweep as we moved down the street.
Mother was allowed Murphy's General Store, and Father
took in the bank and the harness shop. Mother went in to
look for a hat at the milliner's and came out with a frothy
pink calendar and no hat. I went to Lee's Café, and Grandfather went to the Commercial Hotel.

After that it was open season.

Mother might go into the dry-goods store for some ribbon and Father would try the hardware store, while I went
down the side street to see if the cream separator and Delco
dealer was at home.

Meanwhile Grandfather went to Olsen's Blacksmith
Shop while I visited his son, who was trying to make a small
garage pay. There was Medd's Tailor Shop and Liddell's
General Store, where we didn't deal regularly and where I
was expected to look innocent and ask for a calendar.

We also had Ab Walker's Furniture and Undertaking
Parlor, the barbershop, which usually put out an exotic
one, and the feed store. Father had probably already picked
up one the gristmill offered during one of his trips to the
village.

There were extra places, such as the insurance agent;
sometimes the station agent had calendars advertising express, and the livery stable used to put out enormous ones
with large figures which Grandfather favored. From my uncle at his general store I received a large "Old Chum" calendar with two old gentlemen in the picture smoking church-
warden pipes.

Father used to scout around and get a binder-twine calendar and Mother always came away with a picture of an
English flower garden from the drugstore.

On the way home the sleigh box was fairly bristling with

calendars in tubes and packages. I grabbed an armful and raced for the kitchen door, tearing off my outer clothes and attacking the selection. What an assortment!

Mother burned one in the stove one year, although I had a good look at it before she did. It was a very pretty girl wearing tights, which Grandfather said he wanted for his room.

"Act your age," she snapped at Grandfather, who sat back rocking in his chair with his eyes twinkling while the pretty girl went up in smoke.

The calendars were put on the sideboard or top of the sewing machine and admired for a few days. Supplementary ones came from the creamery and the bake-wagon man, and we got a few in the mail from fire insurance companies.

We also received calendars from implement dealers in the county town, and by the time the Dr. Chase and Dodd's medicine almanacs arrived there would be a neat pile of them. Visitors admired and I guess envied us a bit for such an extensive collection.

Just before New Year's Day, Mother started looking the place over with an eye to the distribution of the calendars. It was a practical form of redecoration for the new year.

First of all, some of the pictures had to be salvaged. They could be used to replace some which had been framed in former years and were suffering from age. Most of them after a certain time had a habit of fading or else wrinkling under the glass of the frames. Of course we grew tired of them as well.

I was bound to get an inspirational picture such as a biblical scene and, as a concession to my age, what might be called a cute one with children and animals. The front parlor would get a scene of Niagara Falls or a snow-capped mountain. Mother tried to get an English flower garden for the kitchen. This was solace for a stormy day in winter.

The new calendars were spread around in a somewhat different way. The one from the creamery with the big letters on it went into the pantry. Mother each week noted on it the amount received for the butter and eggs. I don't think she ever totaled the figures at the end of the year, but from some ingrained habit recorded each week's total.

A very large calendar was always hung on the cellar door. It had a purpose—covering up the fact that the door once had been an outside one and that the filling where the window had been was somewhat less than artistic. Over the sideboard there was the prettiest calendar, usually a girl in a cartwheel hat, feeding a dog or patting a horse. This balanced the English flower garden on the other side of the room.

Another calendar hung conveniently under the magazine rack on the wall over the couch. This was for consultation purposes and was placed in such a way that a person had to only lean up to check dates. Grandfather used it a lot.

There was always a calendar in the front hall. This covered the spot where a chimney each winter leaked liquid soot. The front bedroom was given a dignified one which would be in harmony with its cold and unused feeling. There were usually several small ones placed in the front parlor to balance up the samplers and the forbidding aspects of frowning ancestors in ornate gilt frames.

Mother always took a calendar with babies on it for the big bedroom. Grandfather liked pictures of animals if he couldn't get one with pretty and saucy girls.

I always tried to get an extra one if possible, with a hunting scene such as a favorite called "Stag at Bay" with a pack of snarling hounds or wolves around a cornered buck or elk stag.

The painting of a moose which an insurance firm sent out always bothered my mother, because secretly I think she thought it was a fake. It didn't seem possible any animal could look like that.

The binder-twine calendar, which always managed in an unsubtle way to contain an illustration of the product, was hung in the driving shed. One of the less attractive calendars was hung in the granary, but only the back of the pad was used, usually on threshing day, to tally bushels of grain threshed.

Father took the calendar with the largest calendar pad, usually one from an implement firm or a tobacco company, and hung it on the inside of a wall cabinet in the horse stable.

Here he dutifully recorded the intimate details of the families of stock on the farm. He consulted it almost daily, adding pertinent facts of birth and breeding. To the casual observer it was a mass of scribbled hieroglyphics, but the secrets were revealed to him at a casual glance.

The leaves of the pad were never to be removed because he needed them for verification or back checking. The only time I ever saw him in what you might call the white heat of anger was when a hired man tore off the pages and updated the calendar.

That was a difficult year and inspired him to carry a small, black pocket book in the watch pocket of the bib of his overalls where he duplicated the figures but he still kept the calendar. It seemed to be handier!

In the month of January visitors came and were politely curious about the calendars. Some boasted conquests of new calendars because they made special trips to neighboring towns. Mother's response was simply, "Oh well, we don't bother much about calendars. They're handy to have, but I wouldn't go to any special trouble to get more than we have."

On the other hand, when a visitor exclaimed over a particular calendar in what seemed to be a trace of envy she almost purred, "Yes, they are nice, aren't they? I do think they brighten up the place this time of year."

Then Grandfather would add, much to her consternation, "But you should have seen the ones she burnt!"

You would hardly expect intolerance in connection with calendars. It happened in a strange way!

Each year my mother bought a religious calendar. It was put out by a Catholic Missionary Society. The pictures concerned white-robed missionaries with colored children against tropical backgrounds. The pad had crossed fish through Fridays and abstinence days, which were usually the ones before holy days. In addition there was a lot of information about saints I had never heard of before. It came in handy for reading when everything else was exhausted, or after a mission at the church when youthful zeal embraced the idea of my becoming a missionary.

Mother used it constantly as a point of reference.

One day when I was going by the white-brick church I saw the Reverend McPherson struggling with a ladder on the icy front step of the church. Now I had a nodding acquaintance with the tall gentleman, and had always dutifully called him "sir," although I could never understand why we didn't say "Reverend" since we called our priest "Father." He looked so helpless skidding on the ice and waving the ladder that I forgot my shyness and, dropping the schoolbooks, hurried to help him.

While I steadied the ladder and murmured Catholic prayers so I wouldn't let it slip and worried that such prayers might be out of place on Methodist property, he ascended and fixed the window.

"Thank you, boy," he said, and peered at me, and, I am certain, mistook me for one of his own congregation, because he told me to wait a minute and went into the church. When he came out, he handed me a rolled-up cylinder, which I examined as soon as I was out of his sight.

It turned out to be a calendar, and since this was in season I went home joyfully with the loot. It was issued by the Band of Hope, a young people's group. There were some fat angels winging around a golden-haired boy in a white gown. In the corner a leering devil with a forked tail and sprightly ears held a large bottle with three X's on it. Underneath the picture said, GUARDING INNOCENCE FROM THE DEMON.

I hung it up proudly. Mother smiled and didn't say anything except that Reverend McPherson was a kind man. Father looked at it and laughed. My grandfather, however, was enraged.

"It's that damned temperance outfit," he exclaimed, reaching for it; but Mother pushed him away.

After I went to bed he kept on niff-nawing about it being a Protestant calendar. I distinctly heard Mother say, "But temperance, Pa, is a good thing for Catholics as well as Protestants."

He went to bed muttering. The calendar was there for a week, and then one day it vanished. I was furious, and Grandfather said he was sorry the calendar had fallen on the floor and got all dirty, and he gave me one from the hardware store with a dog stalking a deer.

It didn't satisfy me until Mother produced a bribe of a large piece of fresh chocolate cake and a glass of milk, murmuring, "Don't think your grandfather is prejudiced against Protestants or Methodists . . . it's just that he can't stand temperance."

CHAPTER 13

DEATH IN THE COUNTRY

Catholics and Methodists alike were always hearing about
the good life and how man should live by love and charity.
I knew a man who died in our community because he had
nothing to live for when hatred went out of his life.

Wee Angus was one of those individuals born with a
small body of wiry propensity from solid Presbyterian parents. A flaring, hot temper accompanied a tongue that was
apt to exclaim in bitter, acid tones before his mind started
to function properly.

His cousin Black Dan was the exact opposite. Dan was
born with a big frame, a pleasant countenance and a tongue
as smooth as silk to mask the rage that may have been in
his heart. He was a Methodist.

They say the enmity began between the two of them
while they were at school. Angus worked hard and Black
Dan charmed his way through.

They started courting the same girl. Margaret Macrae
was a tomboy in the days when it was considered unlady-
like to show even an ankle. Redheaded, with freckles on a
pale, white face, she was known to have the laughingest
eyes in the township.

Margaret married Black Dan. People said it was because

her parents insisted she marry a Methodist. It was a blow to Angus, who was alone after the death of his mother. He seemed to shrivel up, and his tongue became even more caustic.

After a number of years the feud became an accepted thing. Black Dan was elected councilor. Poor Angus lost most of his herd of cows that year. Because of infection, they had to be destroyed. He sold fifty acres of grassland, and a year later the railroad built a spur through it. Misfortune seemed to dog him but he never complained about ill luck. His hatred and bile were reserved especially for Black Dan.

Margaret died when her second child was born. It was a terrible blow to Angus. It was a shock to Dan, because as far as anyone could tell they were a devoted couple. Angus went to the funeral, and from that day on his hue and cry was about the cruel way Dan had treated her.

The years slipped by and Angus had a bad cold and contracted pneumonia. It was Dr. Jamieson who told us about the way Angus died.

"It was Black Dan killed him. That and charity. I was attending Angus and I couldn't understand how he managed to hold on.

"One day I asked him how he felt and he said he knew I was expecting him to die but not to worry about it. He swore he wasn't going to give Black Dan the laugh on him. He promised he would be around when Dan was in his grave.

"Then two days later Black Dan came in with his son Alex. The boy was a good size and he had Margaret's features and red hair."

Dr. Jamieson paused and scratched his head as if perplexed.

"After they left I went in to see Angus. He was lying

quiet, and he didn't say anything for some time. Finally he told me Black Dan had come to say he felt badly about the squabbles they had had over the years and suggested they make friends.

"Wee Angus raised up in bed then and said with tears in his eyes, 'And Doc, that boy isn't named Alex. Maggie christened the lad Angus, but the blackhearted devil never told anybody.'"

I can still see the doctor putting on his old black hat as he stood up and said, "Angus just slumped back on the pillow then and said he was tired and that I must never trust a Scotchman who went to the Methodist church, and in five minutes he was dead. You see, hatred could keep him alive, but when that went he lost the will to live."

Death was an ever present factor in the country. It was a part of the recognized pattern for seasons and animals and people. It touched our lives and in the close restriction of our living, it could not be ignored.

"Ben Hagen died yesterday from lockjaw."

That could be carelessness, because Ben was a rushing man who would never stop to take precautions after stepping on a rusty spike in the farmyard.

"Big Ned Macdonald died at home last night. The funeral is on Tuesday."

There was no sadness in hearing this. He was over ninety and you remembered the perpetual question of why they called him Big Ned, when you saw him, frail and round-shouldered, shuffling down the Main Street of Clover to the post office.

But there was a difference in the funerals of these two men. It was a shared fact, because our community went to all wakes and all funerals, irrespective of religion or season. It was common to have three Catholic pallbearers and three Protestant.

When they waked and buried Ben Hagen, the men of his age, about forty and with growing families, seemed to be particularly touched. They knew they lived in the shadow of the same danger. They remembered the hands scraped and bleeding from the machinery that they had merely wrapped in a dirty cloth. They murmured questions:

"When did he see the doctor?"

"When did they take him to the hospital?"

And the wives of such men wore frowns of concern. They saw the five children of Ben Hagen and the frightened wife who at one time had narrowly escaped TB, and they wondered where they stood on the lottery.

But it was a different thing on the sun-freckled day of fall when Big Ned was buried. Men and women came to pay their respects to a man who was a legend. This was a brawling, hearty Scotsman who had carried a plow and a bag of meal from the railroad station on his back. This was a man who never backed down from a fight, who captained a side and won in a barn-raising and who danced until dawn at every chance.

They were burying the shadow and the memory and everyone in the community felt this was a full and active man who had made our place better for just being.

Yet there were old men as well at the funeral who sucked at pipes and conversed in low tones and talked about "Neddie" and tried to forget that the law of years and averages was moving up rapidly on them.

Epitaphs were written in the conversations of wakes, for while the women sat in the front parlor and talked in low tones, the men filled the kitchen and the back kitchen.

While an undertaker or a clergyman was expected to walk in the dark way of sorrow, the men accepted death as a fact which couldn't be changed by emotion and so they talked.

"You know, I remember George when we were lads and we went to Handrich to try our entrance examinations . . ."

"Me and George had met two girls from over the county line and we went to see them and when we got to where they lived, their old man was at the gate with a shotgun and I tell you we . . ."

"George was a fair man. I remember when he was first running for the council."

It went on, a running oral tribute to George. Consciously they were trying for the better parts of his life, but they were honest men and found nothing irreverent in slightly ribald stories, because they were a part of the whole man. Finally, in the nodding time that preceded going home, they would cap it with, "But George was a good neighbor."

Yet some would stay on to wake the night through, and in the small hours of the morning when only two or three of his closest friends sat in the warm kitchen, the true story of George was probably told for the first and last time. These were things that his wife and family would probably never know and would not even be shared with the rest of the neighbors.

A funeral where a young mother had died carried a note of its own. You sensed it long before the day of the funeral. This had a bearing on the most vital part of the whole cycle of life and death, and while I was too young to understand, there was an aching void at seeing the young children, baffled and bewildered beyond the point of crying at the loss of something which they in turn were too young to understand.

There were four neglected places in our township. They were the two schools, public and separate and the graveyards of the Catholic and Methodist churches. They were attended to about once a year in a whirlwind fashion by a "bee" of the respective congregations. These energetic souls whizzed through cutting the grass and burdocks and sow thistles, leaving the remains to rot on the ground. In the cemetery they propped up some of the tombstones with the greatest lean on them.

However, there was one place where charity shone. Religion meant absolutely nothing when it came to helping a widow or even a widower. Harvest would be brought in, threshings, silo-fillings, and wood bees were arranged. The community would even speculate as to who would make a suitable mate for the bereaved one. Life had to go on and sorrow could only last so long. It was practical in a situation where farming demanded equal work and service from a man and woman, and to attempt it alone was considered almost suicidal.

The community expected, however, a decent wait of at least twelve months before nuptials, although in a case where there were small children six months was a fair time to wait.

CHAPTER 14

THE MEN OF GOD

There was no doubt about it. The men of God in our township, or at least the official representatives, were Reverend McPherson and Father Morrison. This would seem to place them in positions of power and relative ease. It wasn't that way at all. In fact their jobs were most difficult.

First of all there was the fact most people thought them to be of an almost supernatural order. Protestants might sniff at the celibate way of a priest and Catholics have private opinions of how a man could discharge his pastoral duties while married with a family, but both congregations placed their pastors in positions that now seem almost ridiculous.

Members of the congregations approached the rectories of the pastors with a reverence that seemed to have more in common with pagan theories than Christian practice. There was no such thing as a simple visit or a chat with the occupant. Each one took on the trappings of a pilgrimage, with the visitors stiff and uncomfortable in Sunday dress. I am certain Father Morrison, for instance, must have dreaded these delegations and wished hopefully some of the more congenial members of the flock would simply drop in for a social visit or a game of cards, since euchre was not considered by the Catholics as having a demoralizing effect.

How our rural pastors must have looked with envy to the county town of Handrich where ministers and the priest were curlers and even played golf. The new course had been opened at the bend in the Maitland River which became a handicap. It was rumored some of the members tried to keep the religious out of membership, since it placed a curb on free speech not knowing where they might be playing.

The approach of either men meant a flurry of activity. First of all the lady of the household would estimate the time, having been notified by telephone or that strange communication system of passing along the knowledge, that preceded Mr. Bell's gadget. She would estimate how many calls he had to make and figure if he might be near at dinnertime. Neither man stayed for supper but it was common courtesy to press dinner on them, whether they wanted to stay or not. In fact there is a case on record where Father Morrison was made to eat dinner at the Gibbons farm at eleven-thirty and had another one forced on him at a quarter to one at the Keegs.

Any idea that the reverend gentleman would be present at dinnertime called for a raid on the henhouse. A fat young hen, if she weren't laying, a lazy rooster or a chicken if in season would be offered up on the ceremonial wood block behind the back woodshed. There would be a quick plunge into a kettle of boiling water, and then the feathers literally flew in all directions. Wet chicken feathers would also stick to you, and in some cases it seemed you were merely transferring them from the chicken to yourself.

There was a general impression some of the smarter flocks of chickens that might be running in the more temperate seasons proved the natural wisdom of God's creatures by heading for the swale at the first hint of a clergyman in the neighborhood. They would rather take their chances on the weasel and the fox than the harried housewife.

Some mystical sense associated chicken with religion. Perhaps there was an ancient dietary law that mistily said only chicken was clean enough for God's representatives. Anyhow, the dismembered chicken would be floured and browned in the pan over a hot fire and then left to stew on the stove. In our case, Mother also made hot biscuits. They were quick and tasty and were brought from the oven, light and flaky, with browned tops.

Auxiliary activity would mean an airing of the parlor. In the wintertime the stove was lit with shavings, paper and coal oil and let rage, in hopes the stovepipes wouldn't catch fire. Father and Grandfather were summoned from the fields or the stable and warned to get cleaned up. They always came grumbling.

I often wondered just what Father Morrison thought when he arrived at our place. Father and Grandfather sat like mourners in half Sunday dress, even if it were the middle of a busy season. The house smelled of chicken basking in gravy, and he was escorted almost peremptorily to the front parlor where a slow and awkward conversation began.

"You've been keeping well."

We were assembled in starchy dignity in the parlor. Mother was trying to appear interested in what Father Morrison was saying and still check to see if everything was shipshape. Once she found, to her intense embarrassment, that a pair of bloomers were strung rather picturesquely from one of the projecting candleholders of the parlor organ.

"Oh yes, pretty well."

Grandfather, if he were in bad humor, could put us all on edge by a remark, such as: "Not too bad, but I've been troubled with gas lately."

Mother waded in here with a remark.

"We have had a rather heavy winter."

On this one occasion Grandfather was not to be put off.

"Get old your works don't seem to function as well."

Mother blushed, and Father started scratching his head. She seemed to be the only one concerned. Father Morrison smiled.

"Maybe you've been too hard on your constitution."

The conversation veered off on something else, and Mother rushed to the kitchen because she fancied the chicken was starting to catch. Talk with the priest was always reserved and seemed to go around and around on harmless subjects such as the Christmas concert, the health of some of the older parishioners, or the hope of the priest that some of the congregation might make up a "bee" to look after necessary work at the church.

Priest and minister were poor people. There was no such a thing as "tithes." They really lived on what the congregation gave them, although I think Reverend McPherson was supposed to receive a definite salary of so many hundred dollars. Now, it can be said that neither man suffered real hardship. What they lacked was "cash," because both Protestants and Catholics had a great reluctance to part with money.

Parishioners gave generously of food and wood and their own time for "bees" to make repairs, but they certainly didn't like to toss their money into the Sunday collection. Thus it was when Father Morrison came to call, Father started grumbling about "dues." These were supposed to be given in the spring and fall and were a kind of levy to cover the keep of the pastor and large items of cost, while the Sunday collection was for general day-to-day operations. At Easter and Christmas an envelope was circulated for a pastoral gift. This I suppose was for Father Morrison's own use.

"I paid my dues," Father grumbled as he slopped water at the wash basin, "if he wants more money he takes a fine time to come and disturb a man at his work. How can you pay dues if you don't work?"

Mother just pushed him to the stairway, muttering to me, "I do hope he puts on a clean shirt."

Grandfather teased her.

"It's the cleanness of our souls he's looking for, not putting on fancy duds."

Mother might glare him down to a submissive point, or at least until he went off to change from patched overalls to a clean pair.

"You'll stay to dinner, Father."

Mother made the offer at a time when conversation was at stretching point in the parlor.

"I should be getting on."

He made a half-hearted gesture but there was no use in him trying to argue with fate. It was a slightly malicious point of view with every woman in the congregation that all housekeepers for priests neglected them badly.

Mother was a true magician in whipping up a banquet. She started with a gleaming white tablecloth. Then she took the best silverware from its protective flannel covers in the sideboard. Her wedding china was removed from tissue. The food was superb. We had fried chicken with dumplings that were light and thistledownish in texture, along with pickles from the best side of the cellar rack, mashed potatoes, canned peas picked from the first harvest and put in jars with a touch of fresh mint, and hot biscuits that came wrapped in a white cloth to be unwrapped at the table.

I could never understand where the pie came from. Somehow it appeared and was served, to be followed by a second dessert, and the priest groaned at the sight of canned peaches covered with freshly whipped cream. When the meal was over we sat at the table. Mother didn't dare mention going back into the parlor because that would have taken up too much of the afternoon, and she knew Grandfather was spoiling to get on the old couch in the kitchen for a nap.

Finally, after the priest had smoked a pipe with an apology to Mother, he would say, "I must be getting on."

This was the signal for Father to say, "How is your stock of potatoes?" and then get up without waiting for an answer to go out and put a bag of potatoes and turnips under the buffalo robe in the priest's rig. Meanwhile, Mother had a basket ready with a second chicken in it, sometimes even cooked, and jars of pickles and preserves, and Father Morrison would smile and then, with a gesture to us, kneel down and say a very short prayer while Father stood outside holding the horse.

The priest waved at us and went off down the road. Father would look at Grandfather already dozing on the couch and go up to change his clothes. We knew he was also going to have a few winks of sleep. Mother would clear up the table, humming to herself, because she knew her magic had really worked.

I knew that Father Morrison had gone home, probably to have a sleep. In fact, while the heat stayed on in the parlor I liked to take a book down and lie on the floor and start to read and then drift off myself.

Once I caught a rare insight into the world of these two men by chance. Father Morrison was going to London for a diocesan retreat, and he asked my father to drive him to the station. It was at the time of spring breakup; and

Father took the two-seater democrat, and I was allowed to go along.

When we were passing the white-brick church we caught up to Reverend McPherson. Father stopped, and the minister got on the back seat with the priest. He explained he was going to a County Ministerial Association meeting in Handrich. The roads were bad, and Father had to concentrate in keeping out of potholes.

At first the conversation between the men of God was sketchy, but it warmed up.

"Do you know, Father, I had a heck of a time scratching up enough cash to even buy a railroad ticket to Handrich, and it's only eighteen miles away."

"Mr. McPherson, I am traveling on my housekeeper's salary, which she hasn't been given this month. I would be in quite a dreadful situation if I had to tell the bishop I couldn't attend the annual retreat because I didn't have the money."

They both laughed.

"I suppose, Father, he would have told you to put a bigger charge in your gun and talk about money some Sunday."

"You're right . . . you're right," agreed Father Morrison. "You see, city clergy don't understand that money doesn't come easy in the country. I have to tell them many of these dear people handle very little money in a year, although they're not poor."

Reverend McPherson agreed. They sat silent for a moment or two, and finally I heard the minister say, "But, Father, just between ourselves, don't you get a little fed up on chickens?"

Father Morrison roared, and then I heard him say distinctly, "Now, I have a method, and I don't think it would be any disgrace if I let you in on it."

His voice dropped and I had to strain to hear what he was saying.

"You know Mr. Boyle at the store?"

"Yes, I buy the little bit I can afford there."

"Well, he's a man of discretion. Now what I do is I trade him what I don't use for what I can . . ."

"You mean . . . ?"

"Indeed. He sells the chickens and gives me pork or bacon in return. I presume you belong to the beef ring . . ."

"Oh yes, I could starve without it, although I do think I get a rather high proportion of boiling and stewing beef."

"So do I . . . but I do like a feed of pork now and again . . . of course not on a Friday . . ."

Mr. McPherson chuckled.

"I like pork. You see, I was raised in the country up around Glengarry and, man, there's nothing like fresh side meat . . . incidentally, and I don't want you to pass this on . . . as a matter of principle and without any need for it, I don't eat meat myself on Fridays. Of course if I had more I don't know how my principle would stand up . . ."

When they got off the democrat at the station they were scarcely aware of us. I heard later that Mrs. Flannigan was scandalized because the priest was consorting with the minister and there was rumbling amongst a few of the Methodists about Reverend McPherson later calling on Father Morrison at the rectory.

In a way I suspect I was a witness to a kind of ecumenism on a very practical scale. I know when the shock of Reverend McPherson attending midnight Mass the following year died down, our community had a good feeling about it. I also felt new admiration for my uncle.

CHAPTER 15
COLD, COLD TIMES

I don't suppose there was a single item of homemade invention in our lives as children in the country that caused as much hardship and discomfort, or took such a toll in emotion, as those horrible knitted mittens with a yoke string running over the neck and holding together the appendages.

Strangulating in appearance, they were smothering in spirit. Of course, you had to admit they were constructed and given, in the first place, in a full spirit of generosity combined with a certain note of practicality.

"They're just wonderful for the children. And they're so practical," Mother would murmur, when a pair of two or three appeared from maiden aunts in commemoration of your birthday.

"It was so kind of your Aunt Agnes to go to all this trouble to make you the mittens," she would say, smiling, as she dangled the horrible things.

Grandfather, who, in spite of his age, sensed what a boy was thinking, could add the clincher by saying, "Yes sir, I would sure like to have a pair of those slingshot mitts myself."

Then you knew if they let you use them as slingshots you

wouldn't mind them at all. But they wouldn't! The plan called for a different course of action.

The first matter that made them reprehensible was the fact you couldn't escape them. We tried by putting on as much clothing as possible to avoid having to wear them.

"Here, you forgot to put on those nice mittens Aunt Prunella sent you."

You responded by tossing the yoked things over your shoulders.

"Oh no, young man, there'll be none of that. You'll simply go out and lose them. Then what would I tell your aunt?"

You knew what you would like to tell the aunt, but Mother was starting the threading process. She dangled the mittens and then, scrunching up one, poked it up past your wrist and up your arm. It seemed simple to start at Point A, being the one wrist, and then worm the thing up your arm and over your shoulders and down the other arm and get it to the other hand.

Yet it was rendered virtually impossible by the amount of constricting clothing.

"Aaaaaghhh," you went, expiring on the spot.

"Move," commanded Mother.

You shifted your feet, which by this time were dangling with the tips of your toes only touching the floor.

"At least you could help."

Mother was reddening from the effort. Outside you could hear the rest of the gang chafing as they waited for you. They were anxious to get off to the pond.

Mother changed tactics. She plunged one hand down your collar and started to work it down the arm toward the other hand. It tickled and it choked you and your feet were swinging from the floor and you began to wonder if it were all worth the effort and maybe you should have played sick or something.

"Maaauuugh."

"I think I've almost got it."

Your gasps were getting shorter and more desperate.

"Maaa . . . mmmaaaa."

Appealing to her normal maternal instincts didn't do any good. She was a person with a mission, and she was dedicated.

"Yes, I am almost there."

The strange part of it all is that somehow, by dint of maximum effort, she managed to get the two mitts balanced so they hung about eighteen inches below each hand.

She then stroked your hand into each one and it became apparent that the thumb had a hard ball in it you couldn't get by, and that your aunt tucked the ends of her knitting in such a way that your fingers were cramped, but by this time you were too smart to complain.

"Now you run along and play and you'll be nice and warm . . . and keep those mittens on."

Can you remember trying to play with those flapping things on? They first of all were impossible to wear in a snowball fight because they didn't fit and they soaked up moisture. You kept them on for a time, but finally slipped them off and they flapped around by the umbilical cord and froze and turned into lethal weapons ready to attack you at every move.

No matter how you tried to escape they kept on attacking with a kind of demoniacal energy of their own.

Yet, somehow during the course of the afternoon, the mitts vanished. You didn't have anything to do with it, because you couldn't stand recriminations, and yet they were gone.

"Those nice mitts," exclaimed Mother. "What am I going to tell your aunt?"

Yet there are two facts to complete this story.

There was always another pair lurking in tissue paper in the front spare bedroom.

Also each spring the lost ones would turn up when a snowbank melted, and the strange thing was the yoke cord would not be broken.

They were fiendish inventions.

There were a lot of things that made life miserable or at least uncomfortable in the winter. It's easy to recall the aesthetic things in retrospect, but I suspect we didn't think of them in that way. Life was relatively prosaic . . . and happy and we found ways to surmount unpleasantness.

In wintertime there was the ever-present cold.

Stoves were the heavy guns in our winter battle against cold. Furnaces were something for use in town houses and were considered by most of our elders as being impractical and wasteful of heat.

The kitchen range was a masterpiece of invention. It contained so many practical assets in the way of warming closets, a reservoir to warm water and doors that folded down and could be used for drying things as well as propping your feet.

Our kitchen range, manufactured in Wingham, had shiny nickel in curlicues without practical value but which gave the whole apparatus a much more comfortable appearance. It also had an open-front grate, and certainly no furnace or modern electric range could give the solid comfort of the sight of coals spitting through the iron teeth on the front of the range.

The range, however, required handling. From the time in the morning when Father tried to nurse life from the remaining coals in the ashes, until Mother carefully banked the firebox at night, the range was called upon for different duties. In midmorning, Mother might wash, which meant transferring tepid water from the reservoir to the copper boiler on the stove and replacing the reservoir supply. Some of the clothes would go on the line, some would go on temporary lines strung up in the woodshed or the back kitchen, and still others would be suspended in the space between the back of the range and the pantry wall. This coincided with baking, so that when she stoked up the firebox to fever pitch the whole kitchen would simply glow with heat.

She was fond of referring to it in such terms as "a wonderful baker" or "great heat holder." She polished it until it shone like black wax and the nickel glistened with moonbeams. Once a week the inside of the oven was scrubbed. The ash bucket was taken out twice a week during the dead of winter.

Mother was always complaining about having to lug out the ashes. On the other hand, when one of the men made a raid on the ash bucket, she fluttered around with papers, broom and dustpan waiting to catch the sifted piles of gray that somehow always managed to drift on to the newly scrubbed floor. The range could be adjusted only by someone who knew exactly how to handle all the drafts and checks on it.

If you didn't get all these in proper order you could go out and return to find the kitchen blanketed in smoke, the fire out, or perhaps the pipes on fire. Mother somehow managed to tip and pull and push and fiddle to get things just right. When she was adjusting for baking she looked like a German engineer at a World War I submarine control panel.

My major encounter with the range, apart from putting stockinged feet up on the oven door while doing homework, had to do with kindling. From a tender age, it was my duty to place cedar kindling in the oven for drying. Father liked it cut and shaved fine and then dried to the point where it would practically light by itself. Paper was a luxury and was used sparingly in starting a fire. Coal oil was expensive at twenty cents a gallon and was also dangerous.

The upstairs of the house, except for the attic over the kitchen, was a chilly refrigerator all winter long. You dashed through the front hall, up the stairs, and dove into bed at night. Then began the procedure of getting undressed without letting the cold in under the blankets to stab at your flesh. Prayers were muffled and I often wondered if God could hear through the layers of quilts and blankets.

One of the few times Father ever expressed anger along religious lines was over our boarding the public school teacher. All the people near the public school had reasons for not keeping her. With winter coming on the Higgins family had to move some of their large brood in from the summer kitchen or else let them freeze. This meant displacing Miss Twill or else having her sleep with the children. The Millers and the McAllisters and the Andersons all had excuses, so Mother was finally prevailed upon to take her in.

Miss Twill was a slight, wan-looking person with sculptured brown hair and a nose that stuck out like a log stump in the flat pond of her face. She was nervous and fussy and always complaining about being cold. Mother prevailed on Father, who took an instant dislike to Miss Twill, to do something about heating our frigid upstairs.

Father went to Clover and came back with a large, coffinlike heater that had once been used to heat the Oddfellows Lodge. He put this monster, after an afternoon of wrestling with it, at the head of the stairs. A weird arrangement of stovepipes led through into the visitor's room to a small chimney. It looked as if we were going to enjoy real luxury. We would be about the only people in the township with heat upstairs.

It seemed like a perfect formula, but all the wood had to be lugged in through the kitchen and up the front stairs. Mother hovered in fear that the "graining" on the wainscotting and the staircase might be damaged.

Two things happened. In the first place, the stove glowed with heat and it would roast you within three feet of it. When you moved out of that range of heat the place seemed colder than ever. In the second place, Miss Twill developed a passion for warming her clothes and bedding on the pipes that wound like a puzzle through her room.

One night, when every window in the house was frosted and the chill seemed to be seeping in from everywhere, I grew ambitious and decided I would make that old stove really heat the place. The small, dry sticks were placed carefully and the green wood was on top, and then I added some more dry wood and left the dampers open until the old casket was glowing red on the sides. I dampered it and started seeing how far out from the stove the heat had spread. It seemed very good.

It was at this moment that the teacher reached up while still in bed and dragged down an extra cover which must have been crispy by this time from the heat. Something gave way because the pipes collapsed, and from then on it was sheer bedlam.

Father had to douse the fire with water because we couldn't possibly get the pipes together again. The upstairs smelled of smoke and wet soot, and Miss Twill was moved down to the front bedroom. This room was warm only if you left the kitchen door open. That caused untold trouble. My family liked to play euchre, and the only place for playing was on the kitchen table. Miss Twill didn't approve of euchre, and she was also inclined to need a good deal of sleep. The result was that Miss Twill hovered as if she might force everyone to go away and let her undress and go to bed. In addition she didn't like eating at night, and this snack was the biggest enjoyment of the evening for the rest of us.

The final straw came one evening when there was no card game. It had been postponed because the teacher complained of a headache. By nine o'clock Mother had forcibly made us all go to bed. After I snuggled in, I heard Grandfather mumbling and grumbling and talking to himself in his room. He started walking around, tried to pry the window open, and then went downstairs.

I knew he had probably forgotten to make his visit to the backhouse. He was proud and even the most frigid temperature would not make him use the chamber pot. He would only use it while sick and then under duress.

He had scarcely opened the kitchen door when there came a horrifying shriek. Grandfather came back up the stairs laughing so hard he had to sit on the top stairstep before he could answer Mother.

"What did you do to Miss Twill?"

"I didn't do anything," he gasped, "that one down there was toasting her bare backside at the kitchen stove. I thought she was so damned anxious to get to bed."

Miss Twill left that weekend without thanking any of us and went to live with the Widow Chambers on the side road. I didn't mind seeing her go at all, and besides that she had refused to help me with my homework.

The euchre games were resumed, and even Mother in time laughed about the incident.

CHAPTER 16

THE STARS THAT SHINE

Strange as it may seem, there was always a comforting re-assurance in the sight of stars to a small boy in the cold and solitary nights of a winter-locked valley. To walk in the tight air of frost, when the snow crunched and the taut wires of telephone and fences had a banshee sound, you were aware that the rabbit, fox, and owl were safely hidden, leaving you alone. That's when the stars from their unfathomable distance seemed close in the formality of night.

Through the zero-clinched air they glittered, each tiny and diamond-cold, and yet giving a sense of security in their profusion. The scar-faced moon of contrasting light and shadow was a fickle creature. It came as a rind, leered with the face of mockery in the crescent, flashed into a half-ball, and then filled to a complacent whole. Restless, it waned and left the world again to the continuous and faithful presence of the stars on wintry nights. Even on these occasions when nature indulged in such vagaries as a January thaw, I knew that somewhere above the mysterious and misty canopy they were waiting faithfully.

We knew very little about astronomy. A teacher once called the winking brilliants "tiny windows of heaven." This, in childhood days when we all treasured the notion that heaven, the place of reward for all who lived lives of perfection, was a bejeweled vault of magnificence in the infinity of sky, seemed to be a reasonable explanation. While adding to the mystery of the stars it also contributed to their sparkling majesty.

On a night when I came alone from a visit to a neighbor's or a Valentine concert rehearsal, I walked in the company of the stars. You couldn't overlook them. If you stood still and listened past the sound of the wires and the distant "jing-a-jong" of cutter bells on the concession, there came a small, rushing sound punctuated by tiny, sparking, bubbly pings. It crackled like smothered static, as if someone, somewhere in the vast space, was tantalizing with a jumbled interstellar language.

When the air stood still, as if congealed by breathless cold, there was a temptation to stand on the roadway, encased in the warmth of clothing with the feel of frost on crisp cheeks that made you for a moment feel a delusion that there was warmth in the light of the stars. Common sense made you move. The stars were sirens. Sirens were beautiful hazards associated with a scanty knowledge of how Ulysses had, in a warmer time and place thwarted ones of a different nature. As if to warn, the cold would start to tickle through the wool of mitts and socks, and I would move on. Soon the effort brought the blood surging until the tiny beads of perspiration stood between the skin and the armament of fleece-lined combinations.

The starlit world was a place of shadows of a much different hue from one with the diffusion of a midwinter moon. There was a faint glint of blue in the starlight that shaded into purplish shadows of distorted shapes in the lee of naked trees and the irregular patterns of straight and crooked coil fences. A stand of cornstalks, stripped of cobs and left to frozen rigidity cast weird and jumbled lines on the crystalline cover of the snow. Star shadows were bunty ones in comparison with the full skeletal ones etched by the moon as it moved across the sky.

I doubt if my grandfather thought of the stars in any romantic or mystical way. Just as a sailor depended on them for comfort and a sense of weather, which he found difficult to translate beyond a hunch or a feeling, he used them for directions. As long as he had the reassurance of the Pole Star and Big Dipper he had no hesitation in plunging into the Long Swamp when it was congealed by an icy night. It was a delight for the old man, who spurned the somewhat longer but safer route of the roadway, to renew a youthful sense of adventure, with the insurance of the faithful stars as guides.

There was infinite comfort in coming awake in the thickening cold of the very early morning before the sun had invaded the sky. In the house there was only the sound of partition and paneling protesting the loss of warm comfort. In the kitchen a remnant of a stick spunged as a coal exploded in the ash pit. The curtains held straight and stiff, and the full sense of loneliness of night and space crowded in on my wonderment about the world, the next day, and the mystery of growing up.

It was in that time that the full reassurance of the stars came crowding in. Somehow, there was a sense that the continuing presence of the stars was the link to the past. Did Christopher Columbus, John A. Macdonald, or St. Paul as youngsters stare at the silent vault of heaven and hope that by faithful concentration on the tiny windows of stars they might find answers to the incessant questions of childhood. Sleep came, and even in the light of morning sun I had no despair, because there was certain knowledge that the stars would always be there, faithful and remaining, come sun or changing seasons.

There came occasions, usually on the coldest night of the year, when stars cascaded into the tight cold that were far from celestial. They simply indicated that our pipes were on fire.

The stovepipes always caught on fire sometime during the late winter. It was an annual event, always heralded by Mother in January with reminders.

"I wish you would take down those pipes and clean them one of these days."

This was a first gentle hint. Father nodded. Grandfather would look up and say, "The best way to clean stovepipes in the middle of the winter like this is to open the draft and let her rip. It'll burn the soot right out."

Mother protested: "And set the house on fire!"

Grandfather stoutly defended his theory.

"Not a bit of it. You damper the fire too much and that's why the pipes get sooty. If you let the draft go in a regular way they wouldn't clog up."

Sometimes he might get up and show how the pipes could be cleaned, but Mother fended him off. He usually managed to rap the pipes with his stick, and when the lids were lifted there was an acrid smell in the kitchen.

"There's not going to be any experimenting here," Mother announced finally. "The first fine day that comes along you must clean the stovepipes."

Father nodded. He always agreed with suggestions about jobs as long as they were for the future. It was the immediate ones that gave him a certain amount of trouble.

"You bet! We'll clean them out as soon as we get a thaw."

Well, the thaws came, but something always interfered. Mother would be baking, with bread in the oven, when he appeared with a stick and a gunny sack wrapped around the end.

"Clean the pipes now."

Her expression was sheer exasperation. "You pick now—

and me with the oven full of bread. Why didn't you mention it this morning?"

He then put the stick and sack outside and came in with a grin. "Didn't think of it this morning."

The chances were he might sit down and wait for the fresh bread to be baked. By the time it came out of the oven, Mother was starting to get dinner. And so it went!

Another favorite time was when she was making cakes and pastries for the midwinter social at the church.

"Why can't you pick some time when I'm not busy?"

Father had an answer. "Well, I can hardly clean the pipes on a day when it's storming outside."

On really cold nights we often heard a rustling sound in the pipes. Mother looked terrified when Father gently tapped them.

"They'll collapse, and you'll set the house on fire."

I suppose there was a certain danger. Upstairs, where the pipe came through the floor before snaking toward the chimney, you could feel the heat of the metal collar, and even the painted floor sometimes bubbled and blistered.

Then it happened.

Father was collected from the stable and his chores and raced for the house. The smoke and flames were belching from the kitchen chimney.

"Get the ladder," shouted Grandfather. "I'll get the salt."

Grandfather had a theory that if you doused salt down the chimney it would stop the fire. Father headed for the kitchen with a bag of saltpeter to throw in the firebox. That was his big theory!

They both tried their theories, and the fire continued, with Mother hurrying upstairs to put wet rags on the floor.

"It'll burn itself out," said Father calmly, "they're good pipes."

Grandfather appeared at this moment however, and he turned the dampers and gave a few raps on the pipe. "Just give it a good cleaning out now," he said purposefully, "I've put salt in the chimney. Works every time."

Then he added a further rap on the pipe, which, unfortunately for him, was one too many. A pipe collapsed. It just disintegrated, and then there was really confusion.

It ended in a rout. The kitchen was a scene of dirty ashes, soot, and smoke. The pipes were cleaned and most of them replaced by ones salvaged from the heater in the spare bedroom.

It was a grim household that night. Father protested he certainly wasn't to blame for letting the pipes go so long without cleaning. A cold silence descended on the room and then Mother got up to investigate a dripping sound. Liquid soot was coming down along the pipe from the ceiling. She went upstairs and came down with a glint in her eye.

"The pipes are leaking soot," she said and then added, "there must be salt or something in the chimney."

Grandfather got up and stretched and went to bed. In fact, I went early to a cold bed.

Next day, chimney and pipes and everything got a thorough cleaning, and I was glad to go to school.

But somehow the stovepipe incident was followed by a day with a jubilant note to it. You never knew when it was coming. You might wake up in the middle of the night and there would be a softness in the wind—playing around the house or swishing through the combing branches of the pine trees.

It might be the puckering noises like babies kissing that came from under the eaves.

Father went down the stairs every morning to the weary winter task of lighting the kitchen stove with a heavy, bone-clumping sound, as his heels in the woolen socks descended on each stair.

On this morning of magic, he walked on the balls of his

feet, and the stairs joined with him instead of frostily protesting. He actually whistled in the kitchen, a siren song
that drew me from the tacky warmth of the featherbed to
the kitchen.

"Good morning . . . good morning . . . up early?"

The salutation was in itself a kind of revelation. Father
was ordinarily a quiet man in the morning. While we lived
in the grip of winter, he approached the stable as if expecting to find disaster. It was usually only after breakfast and
at least three cups of strong, black tea that he expanded
into anything approaching a normal conversational tone.

On this morning, Grandfather strolled out to measure
the woodpile. He inspected the wood in the woodshed and
then stood on the back stoop, letting the wind caress his
beard.

Almost self-consciously, Mother put some seeds in warm
water. In a day or so she placed the sprouted seeds in egg-
shells or tin cans and lined them up on the windowsill to
get the benefit of the warming sun.

That was it. There was a subtle warming influence in the
sun, and down in the ground and in the trunks of the trees
we knew, by the age-old instinct of man, something was
stirring and that the long sleep of nature had reached that
peak where rest had to give way to energy.

On a day like this a farmer took a good look at the ewes,
making sure that they were well watered and fed. He might
even go around tacking on boards to cover a few gaps that
had been allowed to stay open all winter.

There was a great temptation on the way to school to
dawdle. The wind was cold, and the trees and shrubs still
had the look of weathered silver about them, and yet, as we
all straggled down the road, we were looking for signs.

A glimpse of a sleek muskrat bobbing up in the black
patch of open water in the creek could send us dancing
along with joy. We did comb through the pussy willows

and, finding some that had burst just slightly, grabbed them in glee to take them along to school.

These pussy willows were significant. The teacher stood great bunches in corn-syrup tins, where the intense heat of the room in time induced them to burst out like silvery worms on the reddish twigs. They did something else, however, which was even more important. They gave the teacher, a city girl, the contagion of our feeling about the break of the winter.

She would start to edge the blackboard with chalked sketches of various kinds of flowers, or she might cut out flowers to paste against the lower windows.

We went home with a feeling as if spring were upon us. Some of the hardier ones with bravado carried their caps until the wind made them replace the covering.

The feeling of the day stayed with us during supper. As I remember it, we always had something special for supper that night . . . a precious jar of wild strawberries might be opened. Mother might start supper off with soup made from her home-canned tomatoes, and it was a lively pink with the darker red chunks of tomato still floating in it, each bowl carrying a blob of butter melting as it came to your place, and waiting to be stirred in with hefty chunks of fresh-baked bread.

Some time during that night I used to wake up and hear the wind again, but it had gone back to a harsher sound. It grated now and sighed in the branches of the pine tree and snarled again in the eaves. There was often a skift of snow by morning, but somehow it didn't matter.

You knew, with a jubilant feeling, you were on your way out of the smothering hand of winter to the time of lilacs and blossoms and soft, caressing winds.

The March wind could snarl as much as he wanted, but you had lost your inner fear. There was hope now!

CHAPTER 17
COUNTRY CUSTOMS

There were a number of things which could be labeled as
country customs. Seating arrangements, for instance, were
a very important matter. It happened in the general store
operated by my uncle. The older men had their choice of
the three battered armchairs. Three cronies for years pecked
at those chairs with their jackknives as tattooing emblems
of ownership. When one died his chair was taken over by
his brother. The slightly younger men sat on the nail kegs
and packing cases, ringed around the front of the old
heater. Newcomers and youths were expected to sit on the
floor with their backs to the counters.

At both the Methodist and Catholic church there was a
definite pattern to the seating.

Bankers, storekeepers, and politicians were expected to sit
in the front seats. In fact, there was a ritual about the whole
affair. Few people bothered to go into church, especially in
the fine weather, until the front pews were occupied.
The center or body of the church took up the rank and file
of the churchgoers. The back seats were the place where
the young men, bachelors, and widowers congregated. They
waited on the lawn or in the church shed until services
started and then raced for the back seats. It was almost a

sign of manhood for a young man to leave the family pew and sit at the back of the church.

Girls were never as fortunate as young men. They had to stay with the family if they couldn't get into the choir. For a young woman to sit with the family of the young man she was keeping company with was considered by some people to be a bit on the bold side. It was literally a sign of engagement.

At dances in the township hall it was generally agreed that older women and women with children sat at the back of the hall. From this sort of neutral position near the heat pipes from the furnace and the big gasoline lamp, they had the ringside seats for the affair. Older men and husbands clustered around in the furnace room, finally yielding to attendance in the hall because of a constant stream of smaller children appearing with messages such as: "Mummy says if you don't come in and dance with her she's going home."

The young women, even the ones escorted by dates, vanished into a makeshift cloakroom arranged in the corner of the hall by draping curtains from the ceiling. They tittered and giggled and laughed and finally came out as a group to sit along the far wall. The escorts clustered around the ticket taker, pretending to be in earnest conversation with each other, and trying to ignore the girls, who in turn seemed to be interested only in each other.

On the raised stand the five-piece orchestra manfully and somewhat discordantly played the tunes of the day. Most of our musicians played by ear. Unfortunately there was a great difference in the ears, but a musical group was on pretty safe ground if it included a good drummer who managed to keep the same steady beat as the pianist. A saxophone was also included for class, because even at this date the success of Rudy Vallee had percolated to our remote community.

The band leader always had a problem in getting the affair started. He had girls to the left of him, mothers ahead of him and boys to the right of him. The fathers were still either in the furnace room or the horse shed. The girls pretended not to be looking at the boys. The mothers tried to keep the children off the floor. The orchestra played on, giving a sort of sample of the new fox trot they were trying to learn. Finally in desperation the band leader called, "Everybody up for a Paul Jones."

Boys raced to make sure someone else didn't ask their girls. Mothers sent ultimatums to husbands. The band leader beamed, and the difficulty was over.

The opening day of school created some interesting problems for a new teacher. The big boys crowded into the back seats, appropriating some for the bigger girls. I don't think they considered beauty. Size must have counted in the "staking out" process. Thus it was the smaller pupils kept getting pushed along the line until they wound up in the front seats. A veteran teacher would come in and take one look at the situation and start sorting them out. Some had different plans. One distrustful soul kept class members apart. Another would try and keep relatives apart.

A new teacher had her problems, however.

"What's your name?"

"John Burns."

"Up to this seat."

Then the comedy started. The seat was too small. He had a bad neck and had to avoid drafts from the window. Another one had a sore leg and must sit with his leg out of the seat. The open space around the box stove was a perfect place for him to sit. We knew he simply wanted to be close to the box stove in the wintertime. Some teachers could be reduced to tears. There was one determined teacher, a mite with a temper and a voice like a woods boss, who made five of the bigger boys sit in the primer seats for a whole week. Even she gave up, however, when one of the lads standing up to answer a question took the seat with him, having industriously removed the screw-nails from the floor.

Even at home there were definite seating arrangements. A rocking chair that stood between the kitchen window and the front of the range was tacitly understood to be Grandfather's. If visitors sat down in it, and that included even Father Morrison, he would act like a broody hen frightened from a nest. Grandfather found excuses to get his pipe or tobacco or a splinter to be lit in the front of the stove. Mother, smiling at the visitor, tried to disguise warning signals to her unhappy parent.

We had one of those old-fashioned reclining chairs. It had a set of faded bronze cushions and a rod arrangement in the back would allow a certain tilting. This was the favorite chair of my father. He would draw it up to the table, adjust it to half reclining with a muttered complaint about whoever had changed it, and then sit down to read the newspaper. Mother used a rocker with a high back and without arms. This allowed her to slide off without any encumbrance when a pot threatened to boil over or a child gave a cry of distress.

Joe and Annie were a married couple who must have agreed early in life that they were never going to sit together. At church, about a year after they were married, Joe went back to sit with his family, and she sat with hers. Even when the rest of the families had passed away they continued to occupy separate seats. As they say, the unusual becomes commonplace after you see it often enough. It was only a visitor who might comment about their sitting apart.

They had another peculiarity. Joe drove a double buggy

and a double cutter. Joe drove from the front seat and Annie rode in the back seat. Joe didn't yield to the temptation of a car for some time. Finally he bought one of those big, black biscuit-box Model T sedans that had a door on one side and two individual seats in front as well as a full-length back seat. Annie rode in the back seat. Joe drove, and at night they used to have a light on inside the car. The neighbors said it looked like a rolling aquarium.

Seating arrangements were important in the country. One of the choirmasters in the village got himself into trouble because it developed he was placing all the pretty girls close to himself and relegating the homely ones to the back row. He called it "harmonic ensemble" or something like that. The board of trustees of the church took a dim view of it, however, when one of the members of the choir, engaged to a curate, was found to be sharing a seat with the choirmaster. It developed she was completely tone-deaf.

There were other details about seating arrangements. At a fowl supper or strawberry social you took pains to be as close to the kitchen as possible, preferably near where your mother was serving or at least a woman relative. The strangers were the ones who were left to the seats at the ends of the tables farthest away from the kitchen.

Seating was important in a lot of ways.

One of the most pleasant winter customs took place before radio started to entertain, and in the long, winter nights when neighbors thought nothing of walking across a snowy field for an evening of conversation and euchre. Some of the local people had an aversion to playing cards but found diversion in checkers, crokinole, or even dominoes. A local church elder who refused to play euchre was once convinced to try "baseball." Although playing cards were used, the threshing gang persuaded him that "baseball" was a harmless game. He persisted in this for two winters until someone inadvertently told him that the game he was playing was one of the more dangerous forms of poker.

The custom I liked most was, however, a by-product of the social evening. It was the lunch. The strange thing was the fact that to hear the visitors talk, you could actually think they were insulted by the idea of having a lunch. It started something like this:

"Well," spoke up Neighbor Higgins, who, by the way, did not play cards on Sunday or after twelve on a Saturday night, leaning back from the table and taking a watch from his pocket, "I think it's about time for us to be moseying along and let you folks get some sleep."

Father would glance at the clock, his eye sweeping back in a signal to Mother, "Lots of time. Just chores tomorrow, we're not going to the bush."

Another hand would be dealt out by Father, and another game would start. Mother would take advantage of his dealing out the cards to put fresh water in the tea kettle and push it up forward on the stove.

"Now, what are you doing?" Mrs. Higgins would ask.

Mother smiled at her and, sitting down, picked up the cards. The play would brisk up, and then the kettle purred and started steaming. This was the signal for Mother to nod at me to take over her hand. There was an interesting thing about playing cards with the neighbors. Father and Mother would play partners, and Grandfather and Mother would play partners. Father and Grandfather never played together. I understand they once did, and it almost ended in complete bloodshed. There was another thing. At most neighbors', the husband partnered with the neighbor's wife and the visiting male was a partner with the hostess. Not at our place!

There was a hazard in playing at this time because the

guests started to lose interest in the cards and look to my mother, all the time protesting against having a lunch.

"Take it up," I might say boldly, and Father would glower at me, while Mrs. Higgins, her eyes straying to the pantry, would say, "Now, you mustn't go to any trouble. We had a late supper and . . ."

From the pantry came the muffled sound of Mother. "I'm not fussing at all. It's just a matter of a bite to eat. Just a bit and a nice cup of tea for that cold walk home."

Meanwhile I was probably euchred, and Father was grunting and mumbling under his breath.

"You didn't even have the right bower, and you ordered it up."

Higgins wasn't paying much attention either. He had spotted the cold ham Mother was slicing at the sideboard. It had been cured with brown sugar and a secret solution and then wrapped in brown paper and buried in a bin of oats to dry out and cure. She had cooked it by gently simmering it, skinning the crusted hide from it, and then browning it in the oven under a solution of honey, mustard, and blackstrap. I could see his mouth watering.

"By golly, you sure can do a ham up nicely."

By this time I was dealing, and no one was paying any attention to the cards. Mrs. Higgins, who shouldered an edge of anger at her husband's remark, would say, "Now, is this nice? We're neglecting Harry and his game of cards."

It was my game! They lost interest, or if they played, they were watching Mother. Finally even I gave up, putting the cards away. Higgins and Father pushed away from the table, and Grandfather, who had been lying on the sofa, swung his feet down and sat waiting. Mrs. Higgins set out plates, cups and saucers on the table. Mother steeped the tea and vanished into the cellar. She brought up the chilled jars of pickles and preserves. There was an unwritten law that on such an occasion new jars were opened, in the accepted manner of gamblers who wanted to play with sealed decks.

"Now, I thought you said you weren't going to any trouble," was Higgins' usual remark, "but by the blue blazes this looks like too much trouble for me."

Father felt called upon to say something at this point.

"Nah, there's no fussing here. We usually have a bite to eat before we go to bed."

This was followed by a discussion on the virtues of having something in your stomach to help sleep along. Higgins related how he once spent a sleepless night visiting some relatives of his wife where they didn't believe in eating before going to bed.

"Thin-blooded people, I suppose," was a typical remark from Grandfather, who had never really cottoned to Mrs. Higgins after she had once confiscated a bottle of whiskey and poured it out, thinking it belonged to her husband, when she found it in their cutter on the night of a school concert. Needless to say it had been my grandfather's property.

This brought Mrs. Higgins to a dilemma. Defense of her relatives might cast aspersions on the lunch my mother was preparing.

"Well, everyone is entitled to their own opinions."

After this diplomatic remark we sat down to the lunch. On a large platter there was sliced ham and perhaps some cold roast beef and usually a few slices of head cheese. The homemade bread, chunky because it was hard to cut when fresh, would be piled up with a plate carrying a fresh pat of butter about the size of your hand and neatly ridged and firm from having been sitting in the chill of the pantry. When you applied it to the bread it skidded into lumps, picking up crumbs. There were always pickles. Cold meat just wouldn't be proper without pickles.

Mother used to make pickles that came out dark green, because of a judicious use of a bit of food coloring, but which were so crisp that they almost exploded when you bit into them, and they carried a taste of cinnamon. I think she called them icicles, and they were her pride and joy, being the result of a recipe handed down from her own grandmother. Of course, there were also dishes of crock-pickles, with onions in them that tasted faintly of mustard and cider vinegar. Complementing these were dishes of spicy chili sauce and corn relish, the yellow kernels contrasting with the red strips of pepper sprinkled through them. Sometimes we had chopped cabbage bathed in homemade dressing or pickled red cabbage. With an eye to color, there might be a dish of tender young carrots preserved in a sweet-and-sour sauce, or yellow beans in mustard sauce with plenty of grainy little spices on them. There was always a cake, usually a chocolate one, with a large pitcher of cold milk beside it and a plate of tarts and shortbread. A bowl was filled with spicy crab apples, and when we had seemingly gorged ourselves, lacing the whole thing with tea that was a dark red color, Mother appeared with nappies filled with home-preserved raspberries or strawberries, each one crowned by a puff of whipped cream. It was magic. I don't know when she prepared it all, but it came.

When it was over, and everyone sat in bloated comfort, I slipped into the shadows to try and avoid the nod of command to go to bed. I was safe as long as I didn't look up, because they didn't dare order me to bed. That would shatter the spell. Finally Mrs. Higgins broke the soft silence by saying in a tone that approached a groan, "Well, I suppose we better go." They floated off into the wintry night, and I scurried to bed, to listen dreamily to the sound of dishes being redded up and then to slide into a world of fantastic dreams, which strangely enough seemed to be all about food.

Grandfather believed that sleep could be induced by a ballast of food. One Friday night, when there were only the two of us at home, he developed a yen for some fried side meat. He had it on the pan frying and put out the plates when he looked at the clock and found we had forgotten to wind it in Mother's absence.

He went to the telephone and cranked for central. Now, our party line closed down at eleven o'clock and the telephone could only be used for emergencies. The male secretary of the rural co-operative telephone company, Nat, slept in the same room as the little switchboard. There was a very large bell to wake him up for an emergency.

"What time is it, Nat?"

Grandfather spluttered and hung up the phone.

"Damn his Methodist hide," he said, and then started to laugh as he started to take the meat from the pan.

"What did he say, Gramp?"

The old man laughed. "He said it was twenty after twelve and time a dogan mick was in bed."

CHAPTER 18

THE AWAKENING

We really came alive at the end of Lent. Although the Methodists didn't officially recognize the Lenten season, they seemed somehow to be in sympathy with the Catholics. It was an unwritten law in our community that the forty days from Ash Wednesday to Holy Saturday shouldn't include too much frivolity, although an exception was made for March 17, St. Patrick's Day.

After that you felt the approach of Easter by the way the teacher, who was going home for the holidays, started stroking the days off the calendar tacked inside her cupboard.

We knew, for instance, she bought a new Easter outfit from the mail-order catalogue.

It was said one woman used to bring Eaton's and Simpson's catalogues to church with her so as to be the first one on the party line when she got home, to broadcast the details and costs of the simple fashion parade.

I remember with affection the house parties that went on. Houses were then big enough for entertaining.

Most of them were two-storied and T-shaped. The crossbar ran parallel with the front roadway. It had a large hall in the center with a spare bedroom and a sitting room on one side and a large parlor and smaller room on the other side. Upstairs there was an assortment of bedrooms.

The shaft of the T was the big kitchen.

"Could you come over tomorrow night?"

Ed Higgins didn't believe in wasting words on the telephone.

"Oh, I guess so. Any reason in particular?"

"Having a bit of a do."

"Well, we'll be there."

Later on, while we were out at the barn or back in the sugar bush, Mother would slip over to see Mrs. Higgins. They were on the next farm. By suppertime, the kitchen at our place would be like a bakery. The next day was the real heart buster. No matter what you did the time seemed to go by in a maddeningly slow way.

"You want me to take something over to Mrs. Higgins?"

Mother wouldn't relent at first. Finally she would give me a wash boiler, scoured for boiling water for tea and coffee, and warn of dire things if I dawdled and didn't come straight back. Chances were that Father would walk over with me.

"Just thought Ed might need a hand."

The big kitchen would be stripped and the range taken out to the back kitchen. Neighbors kept bringing kitchen chairs, and these were ranged around the outside walls. I was sent home to tell Mother that Father was going with Mr. Higgins to borrow an organ.

Small boys might dawdle in getting ready for church, but there was no hesitation when it came to the house party. I sat and watched the lights blazing across the fields at the Higgins' house and grew more and more impatient as I heard people arriving. My folks seemed so slow, but finally we started.

The house party had an atmosphere of its own. Gasoline lamps flared in the rooms downstairs. They had been borrowed from my uncle at the general store.

The mothers congregated in the back kitchen, fussing around the food. The older women either started playing cards in the front parlor or sat in some of the chairs ranged along the kitchen walls. The younger girls darted in and out of the small sitting room, walking self-consciously across the open floor to the kitchen on mysterious errands. The men for the most part hung around on the porch.

Red Sandy came in with his violin, and someone sat down at the organ and they played a jig or a reel.

Finally there was a call for a square dance. It took a lot of effort and one set was made up and then the ice was broken and the fun started in earnest.

The lunch was served at eleven o'clock, the children got sleepy and cranky, and the older folks started going home by midnight.

The house party was over, and there was something like pain in realizing that the Easter holidays were vanishing, but there was comfort in knowing that there was another party on Friday night, and it would last longer, out of deference to the Roman Catholics, because the lunch wouldn't be served until midnight. It was all part of a special Easter feeling.

After Easter the mystical softness of spring affected everyone on the farm. The kitchen door was open. The upstairs windows were up and the curtains billowed out gaily. Mother worked in the velvet cross-drafts caused by the spring breeze through the open doors and windows, and she hummed or sang bits of songs. When she came out to air rugs or bedding on the clothesline, she paused to stand with crossed arms and look across the fields as if trying to breathe deeply and erase winter memories.

I often used to imagine I could hear the grass growing. It may have been the insects and the hum of spring activity, but it seemed natural to believe the grass could make a sound for spring.

Father worked with the stable doors open. In a tuneless way, he whistled. Negotiating the wheelbarrow on the narrow, slippery runway of planks, he would dump a load of manure, drop the handles and stand up straight. Then he paused to look across the sprouting green of fall seeded fields or the drying expanse of fall plowing.

In the pre-school and careless days there was a bubbling excitement in every spring day. It began in the morning when you woke up to find a soft wind caressing the curtains. The air had a sensuous feeling. It persisted through changes that ranged from sunny days to days when an edge of chill touched the breeze.

It was a time when a landscape one day might stand out sharp and clear like an etching in stark colors, but the next day would be soft and steamy and the mist merged with the blush of bloom and greening sense of trees and shrubs.

To a boy without the cares of school, spring was the time when the vitality of a dog seethed, and Snap was happy. He signaled his sympathy by dashing through the barnyard of hens to interrupt their gossipy pecking. A boy found this a reason to make a tour of the limy-smelling henhouse to persuade the broody hens to forget maternal instincts and get out in the air and sunshine.

I liked the henhouse on those days, when the sun poured through the streaked window panes. This was a time to gather the brown and white eggs that were still warm to the touch and felt rough in their newness, and cache them as a later peace offering.

The swale and the creek were magnets for a wanderer. The crows have a spring call that's raucous but tolerable on a day when the frogs sound like liquid springs in their haunts by the pond and the marshy spots. Every creek in spring chuckles and gurgles as if it's being tickled by the sandy bottom.

I had to exercise caution, however. Mother persisted in a dread that any youngster was in dire danger around open water. This added zest to the trip. There was a way of moving through the barnyard to keep the driving shed as a shield.

The big stone pile was an intermediate stopping place. While Snap nosed for mice I ate an apple filched from the cellar. A pit apple always tasted to me the way spring felt . . . earthy and sweet.

The next stop was at the spring. The water glittered and burbled and looked like liquid diamonds. It was so cold it seemed to burn the tongue.

There were all kinds of sounds in that time and of that place. They ranged from the hollow thumpetying of a man pounding stakes to the high and painful wail of fence wire stringing through a staple . . . as a farmer repaired fences for letting out the stabled stock. Incidentally, staples were always called "steeples."

The smokiness of the day came from weathered straw and hay or long grass and weeds being burned off when the ground was still damp enough to prevent a hazard. If the night before had suffered vagaries of cold and a light touch of frost, the smudge pots rolled out smoke across the river on the highlands where some farmers cultivated Northern Spy orchards.

Our trees were toughened to such things as late frosts, and they were old and gnarled like ancient people. The wind had carved and seamed them, but they persisted in bearing fruit without lavish care.

Like most country boys my knowledge of nature was scanty and liberally laced with false knowledge or superstition that had been passed on. It didn't interfere with appreciation for the moment. It didn't prevent a revel in the sight of the reddish tints of awakened beeches, the lime and yellowishness of the maples, or the way the elms were cloudy in their first tender leafing.

This was the time to call Snap and search for the marsh marigolds, called "mush" by Grandfather, and a breathless hope the tiny violets would be delicately blooming. A bunch of flowers and the cached eggs worked wonders with my anxious mother. After all, a boy fresh from a day of such high adventuring had to protect his precious dreaming from a scolding which might break a magic spell.

There were other kinds of adventuring of childhood it takes you a long time to be able to remember without acute distress. That's the way I classify the time Henry Higgins and myself decided to be missionaries and convert Joe Wolf.

It was a perfect Sunday of spring weather. The cat perched on the windowsill enjoying a sun-drenched nap. During dinnertime we allowed ourselves the luxury of spring, even listening for crows.

With the air so soft outside the inside of the house seemed to be heavy and clammy. Grandfather fell asleep on the couch, Father went upstairs to change his Sunday clothes and go to bed as well, and even Mother after finishing the dishes bundled herself on the rocking chair in the parlor and was soon fast asleep. I listened for a time to the flies clammering inside the window blinds and buzzing as if they wanted to get out. I couldn't even kill them because the sound would wake Grandfather.

After a time of boredom I went outside. Snap chased a stick for a short while, and then he got tired and refused to budge. I walked down the laneway idly and without purpose, and that's when Henry Higgins came over. Henry was a good companion because he was smaller than myself and inclined to let me be the leader.

It didn't take long to exhaust our conversation. Then we shied stones at the fence posts and finally landed back in the sugar shanty. We built a small fire, just to do something, and sat down and started talking again.

Henry went to the Methodist church. I went to the Catholic church. Somehow this afternoon in our boredom we started comparing notes about sermons. Something in the weather must have induced the minister and the priest to adopt an adventurous attitude. They had both been zealous about the role of the foreign missions. It would appear that both congregations had been given a liberal application of "Go ye therefore and teach all nations."

This gave us quite a start for discussion. We warmed to the subject, having been induced to more than usual attention by the vehemence of the speakers. I suspect neither of us paid attention to the fact that a collection for foreign missions had been announced for the following Sunday and had taken it for granted some grave situation existed in regard to the non-Christian brethren.

There didn't seem to be much we could do about it, and after the first flaring interest we were more or less discouraged. We sat on. A saucy chipmunk kept eying us. Once an animal of some kind in the underbrush reduced us to trying to conceal from each other fear and terror.

Then the inspiration came.

"Joe Wolf?"

Here was a ready-made candidate for our missionary activities! He was a silent Indian who left the reservation and lived in a small shanty on the river flats near the mouth of the creek. Joe trapped and hunted and did odd jobs for farmers. So far as we knew he didn't attend any church and was probably not even a Christian.

We set out immediately, knowing we could be back before either of the households roused from the Sunday custom of sleeping. The idea gave us so much impetus we ran through the sugar bush and along the river bank. Then we stopped.

"Just what are we going to say to him?" inquired Henry.

This prompted some misgivings, so we sat on some flat stones warmed by the sun and discussed it. There wasn't much discussion because we were somewhat stumped as to how to begin. Then Henry suggested an opening line.

"I can tell him what his Egyptian name is."

"His what?"

"Yes I can too. It's Zapthnath-panneah."

"How do you know?"

"Because my second name is Joseph and my mom said it was Zapthnath-panneah in the Bible."

This seemed like a good opening, and all I could think of was, "What does it profit a man if he gain the whole world and lose his soul?"

It didn't strike us at the time that there wasn't much hope for Joe Wolf of gaining a great deal of the world because he was a squatter to begin with. It also became apparent from a standpoint of knowledge, and in spite of my attendance at catechism classes and Henry at Sunday school, we hadn't learned a great deal.

"I know where they talked about playing cards in the Bible," suggested Henry.

This fascinated me, because I knew quite a few of the older Methodists were opposed to playing cards.

"It doesn't say anything about playing cards in the Bible," I replied scornfully.

"It's when Neb euchred Nezzar . . ." roared Henry.

I grabbed, but he got away.

"If your mother hears you, she'll skelp you."

Henry just laughed.

"My uncle Tom makes up sayings from the Bible, and Ma gets mad. She was spitting the other day because he said Peter was the smallest man on earth because he slept on his watch."

We weren't getting very far in our preparation, so Henry settled down and stopped the foolishness. We compared notes. We both had a working knowledge of God making the earth and about Adam and Eve and the apple and the serpent. Joe Wolf probably knew this already and talking about Noah and the Ark wouldn't do us much good. Henry hopped up on a large stone then and started to recite what he had learned from the Sermon on the Mount, but it seemed sacrilegious so he sat down quietly and we remained quiet for some time, almost afraid to look up at the heavens.

Without looking up, we walked along the river!

We were in front of Joe's shack, and he was sitting out in the sun smoking his pipe. We had to stop.

"Hello, Joe."

He nodded.

"Going fishing?"

We laughed, but he didn't. It was a common fact in Clover township that Joe never laughed. In fact, there were people who said he never smiled. We sat on blocks of wood and discussed the weather and the prospects for trapping. Then we admired the pelts of some foxes hanging on the side of the shack. This seemed to please him and he brought us out a fox pelt, two otters, and several skunks.

Henry broke the ice about our mission.

"We were just wondering . . . Henry and me . . . about . . . well . . . it's really none of our business, but . . . do you go to church, Joe?"

Joe shrugged his shoulders and, with a wave of his pipe to take in trees, river and sky, said, "This is my church."

Considering our recent scare about blasphemy and the sky we didn't comment on what was at that moment a reasonable answer. We went back to talking about the hunting but conversation was scarce and hard to keep going. Joe wasn't the kind of man who encouraged much talk.

"Your name in Egyptian is Zapthnath . . ." said Henry, and added lamely when he couldn't seem to remember the rest of it ". . . it's Zapthnah . . . something . . ."

"I think it's Zapthath . . . knee . . ."

Joe spat and relit his pipe.

"I never met an Egyptian. There used to be a Syrian bought furs from us on the reservation. I guess they must be something alike."

We couldn't say much in reply and by common agreement got up to go. Henry decided on a parting shot.

"Do you ever think about saving your soul?"

Joe Wolf looked at him steadily with his black eyes and said finally, "Indians don't have souls. They have spirits."

He looked stern, so we left in a hurry. Just the same we learned one thing. Joe Wolf could laugh. We heard him even after we passed the mouth of the creek, but there was nothing we could do about it. We couldn't even tell anyone without giving ourselves away about the missionary efforts.

CHAPTER 19

CHILDHOOD

Methodists and Catholics were surprisingly alike when it came to money and its relationship to children. Most of us who grew up then still marvel at the power of a penny—at least the power it had.

Visiting aunts and uncles had a habit of finding pennies in their pockets. Uncles used to slip the pennies to you quietly.

"Here, see if you can use these."

Aunts made a bigger fuss.

I had one aunt who acted as if she were awarding a scholarship, but never gave more than a cent.

"How much did she give you?" asked Grandfather. "She keeps her hand over the money as if it were a silent gift to church for a new bell or something."

"A penny."

He looked surprised and then, leaning over, said, "Next time she does that drop it on the floor where everybody can see it."

I did. She looked flustered and dug around for two more saying, "Oh, I made a mistake."

It didn't work out very well, however. She never gave any more.

Venturing forth on the main street of Clover with a large blackened copper bearing a portrait of Queen Victoria or her son was high adventure. It was also painful. Some inner sense told you as you squeezed at the metal coin that it was a wise idea to have a reserve. Yet, there was the pressure of the moment and the eternal optimism that you might find another or someone might give you one.

The penny customer was an important one. All the stores that could, carried cases of penny goods. This gave you a chance for a vicarious shopping expedition. You could wander into Murphy's store and take a long time in selecting, or even leave without selection. The store was busy, and Murphy believed in pampering youngsters because he was wise enough to know they soon grew into big customers.

If you wanted something you merely looked up, and he came over and said deferentially, "And now, me bye, what can I do for you?" That was a reward.

There was a case of candy and tobacco in the front of the barbershop, but there was a hazard there. The loungers always had a merry time at your expense.

The barber had a flair for selling things that were different. He had gum with picture cards of airplanes from the Great War and licorice with tin whistles attached.

In my uncle's general store there was a large glass case with a crack patched with a strip of adhesive paper. My uncle didn't have time for fancy displays, but since the trade demanded penny goods with a fair number of customers from local separate and public schools he placed boxes of them in the case.

The jawbreakers were black and hard as stone. As they melted they swirled into a variety of colors and ended up with a bitter seed in the center.

They really lasted, whereas the big molasses candies that

were three for a penny were inclined to melt away very quickly. They also had a tendency to disintegrate in your pocket on a hot day.

What we called bull's-eyes were big, vari-colored candies with the consistency of granite.

There were licorice pipes, whistles, plugs, and whips. You bought them and played with them and then took careful bites and kept the stuff in your mouth, pretending it was chewing tobacco, allowing a little to dribble on your chin for the sake of realism. There was also a hard licorice stick that was bitter, and beyond reach because it cost five cents. There were barley sticks of lemon-tasting candy with rings on them.

There were times when I stood pretending a kind of nonchalance as Father did his shopping in Clover, paid his bill, and waited for the clerk to tote up the amount. If it came to an odd number and there were pennies in change, I was in luck.

Then there was always the time when Father, in a good humor, would, without consultation, say to the clerk, "I'll have a nickel's worth of those creams." We drove home with the bag on the seat open between us and Father and I shared in open contentment. It didn't happen very often, but it was truly wonderful when it did.

Protestant and Catholic parents were also united in praise of Puritan virtues. It was an unwritten moral law that children at an early age must accept training in work. Godliness lay in industry, and there was something basically sinful in idleness.

Rich people didn't have to work and were on the road to the fiery place. We, on the other hand, had to be disciplined into a regime of awkward toil, and would someday arrive on the scene of heavenly pleasure. That we would be too worn out to appreciate it was not taken into consideration.

It started with small chores. There was the matter of kindling for the kitchen stove and a supply of wood in the wood box. Chickens had to be fed and watered and we had to gather the eggs.

The blow came when Father interrupted me as I scuffled with Grandfather.

"You seem to have a lot of spare energy these days," he began and, when I didn't answer, continued, "I think it's time you started some regular work around here. Starting tomorrow morning, I want you to milk the red cow each morning and night."

I was stunned.

"You mean?"

"Yes, you'll milk Jessie."

I looked to Mother for help, but she avoided my eyes. Jessie was a monstrous creature we had been trying for three years to get rid of, short of selling to the canners. It would have been an admission by Father he had been beaten in a deal if she went to the packing plant.

None of the neighbors could be induced to buy her, because she was awkward, wandering, and cantankerous.

I had milked some before, but it was different to draw a permanent assignment each night and morning. It was my first work sentence!

That night I had a dream Jessie followed me to school and, when the teacher asked me to recite homework, the cow walked into the room and started doing it for me. This was interrupted by Father calling me as he was on his way down to light the fire in the morning.

I danced and pranced in the cold air and found no comfort in the kitchen. A northeast wind was slashing rain through the bleak dark as we trudged to the barn.

"I tell you boy," Father said, teething into the gale, "when you get the feel of it there's nothing to compare with the satisfaction of hard work."

It was pleasant in the stable with the compressed, animal heat of the night intact. The lanterns shed pale light and the stock attacked the feed with vigor. I stopped to look at the ugly face of my adversary. She seemed to be grinning and skelped at me with the crooked horn.

Father was cheerful and gave me the best milking stool. I moved in gingerly and sat down. The bulk of the cow moved like a great boat shifting with the tide against the pier. The trouble was that I was between the boat and the pier and I dug both fists into her as viciously as possible. She stayed smothering me, as if to underline who was boss, and then moved across to the other side of the stall. This seemed like co-operation until I realized it was merely to give her full room for an assault with her tail.

I can still feel the stinging lash. In a boyish rage I grabbed the tail and curled it. She slammed the pail with her hoof and shifted against me until I sprawled in the gutter. Father went on as if nothing was happening at all.

I could get mad, cry, run away, pray, or try milking again: I combined crying, praying, and milking. I don't know whether it was sympathy for the crying or the power of praying but the bovine harridan let me go ahead.

After what seemed a dreadful length of time, I had only a thin layer of milk on the bottom of the pail. I heard Father finish up the blue cow and move to the roan and still I grabbed and pulled and only a dribble of milk pinged into the pail.

"Here, boy," said my father, "let me show you."

He sprayed the milk in great fashion, showing me how to use my thumb and first finger and the pressure from the palm of my hand. When the pail was half full, he stood up and said, "Now you can finish."

It worked pretty well. I got a rhythmic stroke and the milk streams plunged into the foaming pail and I was feeling quite satisfied. My legs were aching a bit, so I shoved the stool back and edged up. Then Jessie kicked and sent the pail flying. When Father got to me, I was desperately trying to pull her tail off.

Thus began the morning and evening ordeal of milking. They were the two points of my life I dreaded. In time I could milk the old monster and, with constant vigilance, cope with her vagaries.

I found articles in farm magazines and papers suggesting it was wise to drop all dairy cattle and concentrate on beef. A professor who advocated letting the calves run with the cows was my hero. I left all these articles where Father would be sure to read them, but it was a losing battle because we depended on the cream check each week during a majority of the year for the little cash money available.

In the spring when the drover came around I prayed he might buy Jessie. I plotted to let her into the new garden so Mother's wrath might force Father to let the old villain go to the packing plant.

I came home one day from school and met the drover leading Jessie away behind his buggy.

"I'll bet you feel sorry to see this one go," he laughed and I raced to the house.

Mother was smiling.

"Your prayers have been answered. Jessie got in the new corn patch this morning."

"I didn't do it," I said guiltily.

"No," she said gently, "your father left the gate open when he went to the village, and I didn't notice it."

She added softly, "I think he blames me, but I was churning."

That night I started to milk the red heifer, a gentle creature without guile. Somehow, although I couldn't admit it to anyone, I missed the old reprobate.

When I was a small boy, the way people laughed held a wonderful fascination.

Laughter was noticeable in the village. Tim Murphy, whose aproned paunch dominated the general store, always seemed to be laughing. His red nose glinted as he leaned over the counter and demanded in a mock-serious way: "And Mr. Boyle, what can I do for you?" When this produced embarrassment, he leaned back, and his paunch quivered like a nervous drum. Then he rewarded you with a licorice pipe or a glittering bull's-eye candy.

Even Mr. Henderson, the banker, who looked like a gray toothpick in his well-tailored clothes, inquired about a small boy. "And now, young man, are you thinking of negotiating a loan?"

I never quite knew how to answer these rhetorical questions. Experience taught, however, that the best response was a grin. Mr. Henderson would then finger coins with his slender white fingers in his vest pocket and finally bestow a shiny penny with the royal air of presenting a decoration.

I liked walking slowly by the door of the back room of the Commercial Hotel. This was a forbidden place for a youngster, but you were rewarded by the sound of bursts of laughter punctuated by the clinking of glasses. Men would come out smiling and wiping frothy mustaches.

"Well, boy, how are you today?"

The blacksmith, the driver, and the gristmill owner were big men who smoked pipes and black cigars. They laughed with a rolling sound like far-off, happy summer thunder.

Dr. Jamieson was a big man with a face haloed by a great salt-and-pepper beard. He was a busy man who didn't seem to have much time to spare, but now and again he exploded into laughter. People stopped and became caught up in the infection without knowing the cause.

Albert, the fertilizer and lightning-rod salesman, who brought radio to the valley, was a slow starter. It gurgled a bit at first down in his stomach, swelled into a series of convulsive tremors in his chest, and finally exploded into a series of guffaws.

Oscar and Ethel looked as if laughter could be painful. They snickered. Oscar would look off in the distance and twitch his nose like a bunny. Ethel snickered into a handkerchief in a dry way.

Jimmy Janes was a giggler. He started with a series of chuckles deep in his throat that rolled downward until his belly started to slop like a heavey horse, and then he was gone. All you had to do was look at him after that and he would double up holding his stomach, trying to control himself.

Once, in Handrich, with Grandfather, I witnessed a show in the theater. The man who fascinated me gave what he called a lecture on laughter. He started slowly and gave illustrations of the various kinds of laughter. He tittered and giggled and snickered and guffawed. He held the audience in his spell until all he had to do was put on a different expression and the whole place rocked with explosions of laughter.

The exhibition remained with me. Every time I thought of it I would start smiling. This was dangerous because Grandfather had warned me against telling about the show. It had also offered a series of bouncing belles in scanty costumes, and Grandfather was certain that Mother would not approve my having attended.

This must have been in my mind when I volunteered to do a solo skit for the spring concert. It was on the understanding I would practice by myself and make it a surprise. I almost drove the stock into a neurotic state by rehearsal in the stable. On a stump in a clearing, I held forth while Snap cowered in the underbrush.

I was certain that my act would be outstanding until the homemade curtain rolled up and I stood in knock-kneed terror, staring at my neighbors and relatives. Every time I tried to say something my tongue globbed up in my throat. I couldn't get a word out. Then something happened. The audience started to laugh. They roared and I finally bowed and scurried off. The teacher was ecstatic.

"What a clever idea to call it 'Laughter' and make them laugh that way."

I was glad that none of the stock or my dog Snap could talk and give away the secret of what I had practiced for my essay on laughing.

CHAPTER 20

THE VISITORS

I think of them now as pale people. Actually they were called "city relatives." They came as an invading force in the dying days of June or the brisk, hot days of early July. There was a pleasant myth they had come to work for their "keep."

Because the ties of family were strong in those days, they were welcomed as fugitives from the hot inhospitality of city streets. There was a general idea some grave evil lurked in the city during the summer, ready to lead youngsters astray.

Visiting city relatives came usually in two forms. They were either shy and a bit afraid of strange surroundings or overpoweringly brash and conscious of the advantages of the acquired knowledge of city living.

If it was one of the former we breathed easier, aware that there was a certain comfort in being the dispenser of country knowledge. If it turned out to be one of the second kind, your mind immediately savored the thrill of bringing about a comeuppance. In familiar surroundings, this wasn't too hard to manage.

A shy relative was a delight. Commonplace things of farm life could be made quite important to an appreciative audience. Latent acting ability was always present as you walked in front of the bull pen. A city relative didn't have to know the snorting animal was securely stanchioned.

With the proper emphasis, even driving the elderly team of horses could assume some of the glamour of a Roman chariot core when you nudged them into a trot. A walking expedition was pure delight. Threading your way on the clumps of tufted grass in the swale appeared to be dangerous if you happened to reveal the great perils of slipping into the swamp muck. Any city youngster who had only concrete and narrow backyards was awestruck by the fleet of simulated cruisers and vessels of all kinds anchored in the pool.

Few boys and girls could resist a sail on the raft on the pasture pond. The raft was a makeshift affair of two cedar logs with a haphazard arrangement of boards, but then water has always had a lure for children, when not applied for cleansing effect.

The sluggish mudcat and the frogs were supposed to have fierce qualities. A boy was quite daring as he plucked a leech off with apparent disdain for danger. The harmless garter snake assumed some of the deadliness of the rattlesnake or even a small python when you handled it.

A summer vacation was a pleasant affair when you were envied by a visitor. It was a trying one when you drew a brash character who treated you as a grade above an imbecile and wanted to impress everyone with the advantages of city living. Your only defense against this kind of thing was to plan traps.

Usually, if the youngster was poisonous enough or inclined to be fresh with your parents, they allowed you free reign short of physical danger or violence.

In the first place, your brash cousin was vulnerable to the sun. This was a great advantage. It wasn't too difficult to manage to have him misplace his hat before you started on a rafting expedition.

Or a trip to the river swimming hole at high noon on a Sunday, when the sun, blazing down with reflected intensity from the calm water and surrounding rock, could sizzle a pleasant patina of red on a pale skin.

When a city cousin came along, the barn assumed a new role. It was the location for our action and a certain amount of fiction. Ordinary aspects could be made quite extraordinary, when you capitalized on the innocence of the visitors.

This was quite fair, because as a country youngster visiting in the city you were even more vulnerable.

A barn in the summertime has a distinct quality about it. The stalls are vacant except for calves too young for weaning and the bull, a reluctant prisoner in a large box stall, could be counted on to add a thrilling note when you opened the stable door.

"Wh . . . whasat?"

The visitor would shrink back as if going to bolt for the safety of the house. Now, as a youngster, I never felt very comfortable about those massive beasts that carried rings in their noses. There were too many stories about men being gored, which I knew to be true, ever to forget the danger. It was different, however, with an audience and the knowledge that Sir Timothy was held by a strong stanchion behind a plank wall and that the door of sturdy elm was barricaded by two pieces of plank as well.

"That's only the bull."

"The . . . the bull!"

This cousin, who once had me knee-shaking on a side street at dusk in the pastoral city of London, Ontario, with his tales of gangsters and murders, was frightened by the presence of the bull. It made me feel brave, or at least able to put on a bold front.

"Come on down here, and I'll let you look at him."

The cousin would trail along fearfully. Once he passed a certain point it was easier for him to crowd beside me than mentally to plan his escape route. With what I thought was nonchalance, I would turn the knob and let down the door of the manger.

"Crowshhh . . ."

The bull could be counted on to snort and rattle chains and stamp a bit and lurch toward the manger. This reduced a cousin, male or female, to a chattering wreck. Invariably they would cling to you for life and in the case of some of the more buxom girl cousins from the city, it had certain charms.

In the case of my smart-aleck cousin from London, it gave me the greatest sense of revenge. He didn't know, and, in fact, none of them suspected that we were looking at the bull from the safest of all places. They didn't know, either, that every time I did it, the sight of the snorting and glaring monster also chilled my blood a little and left my heart flip-flopping.

The principal thing about the bull episode was it left you master of the situation. You could suggest what you wanted in the way of play. It was amazing, for instance, how many of them thought that pulping roots or fanning grain was really play. I used to wish they would come in the winter when there was really work to do.

Barn cats were always having kittens in improbable places. These half-wild creatures, with their instinct of defense in claws and teeth, never failed to make the cousins desire them. An aunt with a tendency to berate you to your own folks could be neatly paid off by subtly suggesting to

cousins that it was such a shame that they didn't have a
cat.

You offered them a choice of color and gently hinted it
was time they started asserting themselves.

It never failed to create a scene at the end of a day of
visiting and more than one city aunt with a condescending
manner has been reduced to tears by having to take along a
savage little barn kitten to appease a determined child.

Not all visiting cousins were easy to handle. It was just
that in the familiar surroundings of the barn you had a
chance to outwit them.

There was the trap door where the hay was pushed down
from the barn floor. This was invariably open. It was un-
safe; there's no doubt about that. It was just that all of us
knew exactly where it was and avoided it without thinking,
and somehow it always seemed to be a lot of trouble to
cover it up.

In addition to being open, it was usually half plugged
with hay. Straw didn't stick the same way as long-stemmed
timothy or a bundle of alfalfa. It was a simple matter to be
walking across the barn floor and suddenly dare the visitor
as to how far he could jump . . . into the hay. None was
ever hurt, but pride took a nasty bump on the floor of the
stable below.

When my conscience disturbed me, I remembered the
time a tomboy cousin in the city had managed to direct me
into a ladies' washroom. She had also once slipped away
from me in Union Station, to watch from behind a pillar as
I aimlessly wandered around without the slightest notion
of how to get to her house.

For playing without malice, there was also plenty of opportunity.

The granary was a place where a cat might take off in
pursuit of a mouse. It was a unique form of pleasure to try

walking in the piles of grain that shifted and divided under your weight and spread up between your toes and then threatened to engulf you.

There was the pleasure of showing your companions how to chew the newly threshed wheat into a white, gummy substance. They always seemed to want to translate the amount of grain into equations of loaves of bread to be purchased in bakery and grocery. The amounts quoted left them with staggering thoughts of our wealth.

In haying or harvesting time, you could give them a fair idea of your own worth and responsibility. It seemed a great task to be able to unhitch the team, after the wagon had been driven on the floor by someone else. Then you took them around and hitched on the slings and drove carefully on the shouted directions from the mow and the barn floor until the bundle of sheaves or hay was dumped into the waiting mow.

From high up in the barn, where normally the pigeons and the barn swallows stayed, there were peepholes that have a wonderful view over the farm and across the river. It was a precarious trip up the fixed ladder onto the beams when the mows were empty and an easy one when they were filled. A fall into a full mow was a thrill.

Away up in the barn, however, you still had power over your visitors. It was easy to induce one of them to fall into the barley mow sprinkled with ripened Russian thistles, instead of the hay or wheat mow.

It was also simple to let one of them edge over the beam where the pigeon lice were thick. Come to think of it, nothing could take the superiority out of a prideful city cousin quicker than an invasion of bird lice.

Grandfather often helped. On a summer night when scudding black clouds made the moon play hide-and-seek, he welcomed a new audience for his stories about banshees

that wailed at death and the spirits that hovered like supernatural smoke in the old graveyard on the side road.

"Ah, boy, I tell you there's things that roam by night
that a mortal man should fear."

When a visitor was too tough to handle I could always
call for help on my older cousin Joe Alex, in the village. He
had no compunctions about letting a smart fellow slip in
a nasty pigpen, lose his footing in a barnyard, or get a rope
burn in sliding down from the mow. Joe Alex had a gift
for appearing innocent, sympathizing with the victim.

The summer passed and somehow when it came time for
the pale ones, now sporting good coats of tan, to go, I was
sorry. The shy ones had progressed to a new confidence, and
the brash ones had toned down to the point where you
had to admit you were going to miss their companionship.
They slipped back to the mystery they had come from, wiser
from their experience, leaving you a trifle lonely and wondering if you hadn't been a trifle too harsh on them.

We had other visitors as well. These included a relative
from the "Michigan States." It was a long time before I
connected the United States with them at all. This happened because most of the relatives were descended from
uncles or cousins who tired of fighting the bush country of
pioneer days in Ontario and had moved to Michigan. Others had gone, like my grandfather, to work in the lumber
woods of northern Michigan and hadn't come back. It was
rumored that some of them after a winter in the bush had
never been able to get past the fleshpots of Saginaw or Bay
City.

They brought color into our drab valley lives. They
breezed in driving Grey Dorts, Essex, Packards, Hupmobiles and other exotic makes of automobiles in contrast
with the few Model T's in our community. Most of them

wore what seemed like gaudy clothes to contrast with the drab blues and blacks of our Sunday best.

The Michigan State boys were a restless lot, boasting about the way money could be picked up so easily in Deetroit working for Henry Ford. They fascinated the youngsters, charmed the girls especially, and gave great worry to the older people, Methodist and Catholic alike, for their rather flippant approach to religion. Just the same they were welcome at our little church because they showered Father Morrison with American greenbacks, even if they did seem to have a touch of disrespect.

My hero was a cousin called Bill from Bay City. We knew he was coming to spend the summer, and Mother was in a dither because she heard that he was going to the seminary in the fall. The front parlor was aired and painted and the floor varnished to sticky perfection. The walls were decorated with holy pictures, and she even induced Father to make a kneeler that looked like the one Father Morrison used in the sanctuary of the church. She tried to make a shrine out of the spare bedroom, putting some palm around the picture of the Sacred Heart, which had been moved from the landing in the front hallway.

Bill arrived driving a yellow Reo touring with disk wheels. He wore sport clothes and smoked cigarettes and used grease on his hair. This was enough ordinarily to turn Mother, but she was loyal.

"He's just really only a boy," she would say wistfully, "and he'll be safe this fall when he goes into the seminary."

It took courage for her to hear that Bill took skinny dips with the rest of the young people in the Deep Hole at the bend in the river behind our farm. I am sure she said extra decades of the rosary at night, when the girls in the community started finding excuses to visit our place. It was natural because Bill was tall and black-haired with a truly handsome appearance.

"You'd think he would be saying more prayers than he does," she said, finding excuses to have him take things to Father Morrison.

Bill went to dances and parties and was a perfect companion for a growing boy. Grandfather adopted him as a kindred soul because he was always ready at the end of a hot day to take a run into Clover for a visit to the back room of the Commercial Hotel. When they both came home one night singing Grandfather's one song, the ballad, "Bury Me Not on the Lone Prairie," she sat down to write a letter to his mother. Father persuaded her to tear it up. I was glad she did, because by this time Bill had inducted me into the wonderful world of Zane Grey and I wanted to finish his books before he left.

She was practically distraught when he drove a girl home from a dance. She compressed her lips tightly when we heard that it was one of the maids from the Commercial Hotel. It wasn't social snobbery either!

I noticed things however. Bill wasn't always laughing. He spent a lot of time just lying on his back in the grass staring up as if he were trying to peer into the sky. I knew he spent a good deal of time with Father Gibbons in the village and went also to see Father Morrison occasionally and once or twice he spent an evening with Reverend McPherson.

When he left she cried.

"I want to thank you folks for making this a perfect summer. It's my last free one, in a way, because I have definitely decided to enter the seminary next month. This is a wonderful place, and when I get to be a priest I hope I get a parish in the country like this. You may not know it but one of the reasons this is a grand place is because the Methodists and Catholics are so much alike. This place is a lesson."

Mother puzzled over that for a long time. I think it disturbed her a little that the Sunday ball games which Bill had organized were continued. Some Lord's Day Alliance people complained, but Reverend McPherson and Father Morrison didn't encourage them, and somehow the county constable always seemed to be busy when a complaint came in. He did come all the way from Handrich twice, but of course he had telephoned before coming to see if anyone were playing ball. By the time he arrived all the players were sitting peacefully on the front steps of my uncle's general store.

Just the same Mother was greatly relieved when she received an invitation to his ordination. She didn't go, but she carried the notice in her prayer book until it disintegrated. Somewhere along the line I think she must have made a deal with the Lord about that vocation.

CHAPTER 21

THE GAY BACHELORS

All women in the country, married and single, pitted themselves against the challenge presented by bachelors. They would lie, cheat, steal, and connive to make certain an eligible single man was caught in the bonds of matrimony.

Men didn't take part in this kind of thing. They just watched from the sidelines and felt sorry for the quarry. Two men in our community who eluded the wiles of the scheming women were Dr. Jamieson and Joe Broome.

Dr. Jamieson came as a young man to Clover and set up practice. It soon developed into a very heavy one. When he stopped shaving and grew a whisker it added a challenge. He said he didn't have time to shave. There were many spinsters in our township and in the village itself who secretly vowed it wouldn't take them long after marriage to remove the foliage.

Dr. Jamieson was invited to parties, teas, dinners, luncheons, dances, and he ignored them all. He relaxed in the back room of the Commercial Hotel or at the Smoke Hole behind Olsen's Blacksmith Shop or in an occasional card game in the upstairs room over the Medd's Tailor Shop. He went away each year for from two to four weeks and as he said, "Sprinkled wild oats to grow on somebody else's lawn."

Then the stories started. In defense the women circulated a yarn about his having a tubercular wife in Scotland. There was another story that he had lost his love in a shipwreck and had vowed to never marry anyone else. What they all overlooked, I suspect, was his unselfish devotion to medicine.

He once told my father a doctor was like a clergyman and shouldn't marry, adding with a sly wink, "But according to the proverbs, a continual dropping on a very rainy day and a contentious woman are alike."

Once he was trapped by a meeting of the Ladies Aid of one of the Clover churches. He had to call on old Mrs. Dorking only to find that a group of her daughter-in-law's cronies were having a tea. When he came down from the upstairs he was pressed to have a cup of tea. Mrs. Flander was a bossy woman and she took the occasion to ask him rather rudely, "Why have you never married, Doctor?"

Dr. Jamieson is reported to have said, "Aye, it's because I do not trust women. I was in the habit of sleeping in the raw when I was a poor and hard working intern in Glasgow and one night, four burly and husky women nurses rushed in and without ado grabbed me up and set my bare backside on top of a bedpan full of ice and held me there. From that moment on I have nevair trusted women."

He made his exit while they were still gasping but was never asked such a question again.

Yet he was not unkind to women. He was a big man with sprouting black whiskers, liberally sprinkled with gray. His hair always stood up like a wind-ruffled pile of salt and pepper. He carried over 260 pounds on a medium frame with a fair proportion of the weight projecting under a spacious vest. He was gruff, impatient with dawdlers of any kind, quick-tempered, and scornful of incompetence. In spite of this he put up with Tilly as a housekeeper.

Tilly was a loose-jointed creature who didn't seem to be put together properly. She was heavy below and light above and walked in a sidling way. Given to wearing hats with waving ferns or flowers of staggering proportions, she was truly a sight to behold on her way to church.

Product of a succession of foster homes where she had been little more than a slave, she was found by Dr. Jamieson with acute pneumonia, still trying to do her work for a penny-pinching family on the second concession.

The problem with Tilly was she had good intentions but little idea of how to do anything. At her foster homes she had been consigned to scrubbing, fetching, carrying, and polishing. The doctor's home, a large frame house on Main Street, was soon shining and spick and span.

Tilly had difficulty with other aspects of keeping house. The doctor was never seen without a clean shirt after the advent of Tilly, but her mending left a lot to be desired.

Tilly was a plain cook. Dr. Jamieson came to our place to attend an elderly visitor who had taken ill. I can still see him in the kitchen asking for baking soda. He swished up a glass, gulped it down, and grinned when my grandfather said with a smirk, "Jamieson, that would cost two dollars in your office."

"By the blazing herons," he said, sitting down, an act which was unusual in itself, "that Tilly—she makes good tea and toast and anything simple like meat and potatoes, but she wants to be a fancy cook. Tonight she put down in front of me for dessert what she called a trifle. It was no trifle, it was a monumental error."

When Mother started to protest, he put his hand up, "I know, the poor thing is like a crippled sparrow, destined to hobble and wanting desperately to fly."

Tilly certainly wanted to fly.

She was a member of the red-brick Methodist church. She said she liked the way they hated sin.

Tilly didn't confine her activity to the Methodist church, however. When the Roman Catholics or the Baptists had a bake sale or a quilt raffle—or any of the other devices they employed for solvency—she responded. Her favorite source of inspiration was in the women's magazine she used to borrow from the milliner. The milliner who had once made a trip to Paris and had never forgotten, had a habit of marking anything that seemed to have a French flavor and Tilly responded by trying some of the recipes.

Tilly entered many classes at the fall fair. It was a regular ritual with the judges to give her an honorable mention for her preserves or fancy work.

When Dr. Jamieson was going, Mother asked him if he would like some crab apples. They were particularly good that year. The doctor shook his head, then came back and said, "Humm, not many people enter crab apples at the fair, do they?"

Mother assured him they didn't because crab apples were an uncertain crop. He took a bushel of them.

Dr. Jamieson dropped in one fall day to see if the russets were ready. He liked apples and kept some on the buggy or car seat all summer and fall. When my mother asked him how Tilly was keeping, he shook his head.

"The lass is no' well. She's even lost her interest in entering anything at the fair. I don't suppose the judges will mind."

We never thought any more about it, but then the news spread through the township like mad after the fall fair. Tilly had finally won a first prize for preserves. She had entered preserved crab apples. Mother looked smug about it, and Father and Grandfather tried to pry out of her how it had happened.

"Oh dear," said Mother, "you never give up. Now you mustn't repeat this. When the judges were doing the preserves, who appeared in the hall on the night before the fair but the doctor."

Mother smiled and remained silent for a maddeningly long time.

"There were four entries for crab apples. The doctor watched the judges as they looked at the entries. Now all entries are supposed to be secret, but everybody knows most of them. Just as Harold Gibson picked up the first jar of crab apples the doctor said he was very fond of them but in his opinion appearance couldn't really tell. The only way was to sample them.

"They looked a bit startled at this, because women pride themselves on being able to tell by appearance the quality of preserves. To make a long story short, they opened the preserves and sampled them and came to the one the doctor had been holding. They tasted and then they tasted some more and they finally started drinking the syrup to determine what it was. They liked it. Tilly won first prize."

Mother got up and started to clear the dishes.

"Well," said Father finally, "what was it?"

Mother shrugged.

"I couldn't really say but the doctor told me when I was in there next day he hoped Tilly never found out what he really used the prescription brandy for."

Grandfather roared when he heard about it. It took all of Mother's persuasive power to keep him from telling Harold Gibson about it. Harold was a staunch prohibitionist who made an annual practice of enticing Methodist youths to take the temperance pledge.

People used to say that Joe Broome was an odd stick. He lived in a large, square frame house that was weathered to a silvery gray. It had rambling verandas along three sides and sat squarely in the midst of what had once been a delightful rose garden. Wild roses, lacking his mother's attention, fought for space with weeds and broken down arbors. An old stable, where his father once kept fine drivers and two spanking rigs, leaned lazily, as if it didn't have the ambition to fall down.

Joe lived penuriously on a limited income from the estate held rigidly in trusteeship for him. Old Peter Broome, who made his money pirating timber from hard-up farmers, didn't have much faith in his son's business ability. Joe, a lean rail of a man who dressed in old-fashioned clothes inherited from a corpulent father, had something of the appearance of a scarecrow. Because he had a passion for auction sales, coming early and staying late, he gave the further impression of being a scavenger.

Every auctioneer in the district knew Joe. The tall figure looked like a burned jackpine in a forest among an auction crowd. The auctioneer, to warm up the crowd for a choice sale, would point to a handsome gelding or a prize cow and say, "Come on, folks, hurry up and bid before Joe Broome beats you to it."

"A dollar," Joe would shout, and the audience would laugh, and Joe, as if having gone through a ritual, would start prowling around, looking at everything on display. In a small black notebook he would make mysterious markings, oblivious to the crowd of children that followed him.

"Whatcha doin', Joe?"

"Ya never buy nothin', Joe?"

It didn't bother Joe. He was a patient man, and when the sale had worn on and people were starting to thin out, the auctioneer would begin to sell off odd lots. Piling a variety of things, from tin pails to lamps and old-fashioned commode sets, he would shout, "Come on, folks, gotta get this stuff cleaned up. What am I bid? Come on, Joe?"

Joe would bid. The auctioneer would knock it down to him.

"Look at that for value. Joe there, for twenty-five cents, has untold wealth."

People laughed.

"Only junk."

Just the same their laughter sounded hollow. There's a certain amount of the scavenger in all of us. Every driving shed had a collection of odds and ends, bought at auctions with the lame excuse that there was a good hammer in it or a wrench that could be fixed.

It started the bidding. Joe managed to get another lot or two when the bidding slackened, and he always seemed to end up with a small table that had a broken leg or the handles missing. He bought rockers and odd beds of unusual design for very little.

He bought the things that most people in our district didn't want. Every household was crowded with heavy, dark furniture that had carved scroll and spool and fruit designs on it. Every home had a profusion of small tables, inherited from cousins or aunts, which cluttered up hallways. Our people were looking for the kind of furniture that was displayed in the mail-order catalogues, and so Joe accumulated the old stuff. People laughed at the thought of it ever being of any use.

"That house of his must be like a Noah's Ark," commented Ab Walker, the combined funeral director and furniture dealer and cabinetmaker. "If he wants to come along he can help himself to some of the old stuff that I've accumulated in my cellar and in the loft over the stable."

Ab continued to display modern beds in his window and take in the old stuff. Joe continued buying at the auction

sales and then we noticed something was happening at
the Broome place. The verandas were beginning to display
furniture.

"Joe had to move some of the stuff out or else move
himself out," was the comment.

The verandas filled and there were pieces of furniture
piled up beside the stable.

Then one summer Joe bought a music box. It was one of
those old-fashioned ones that played steel disks. The disks
had holes punched in them to catch levers which in turn
played hammers on strings. Joe installed it on the front
porch in a cleared space and entertained himself by playing it almost every evening.

Then something happened which electrified the community. A man stopped one day and bought the music box
for some fabulous amount. The rumors had it for any-
where from $25 to $200. It wasn't the amount that set people on fire. First of all everybody knew he had only paid
$3.00 for it. No one had wanted it. They were thinking of
modern gramophones or one of the new batteryless radios.
The second startling thing was the fact that the music box
had been bought for a museum Henry Ford was establishing near Detroit at a place called Dearborn. Soon rumors
had it Henry Ford himself had come to see Joe.

Next thing a truck took away a load of stuff from Joe's
place and Joe deposited $1000 in the bank. Then came the
day when a large sign reading ANTEEKS was nailed up on a
post at the gateway. Ab Walker had a neat sign lettered
ANTIQUES put up in front of his shop and he had a har-
monium, an organ, and an ornate sideboard displayed in
one window.

Joe didn't change his place a bit. He took the tarpaulin
off the assortment in the backyard, displayed old irons,
lamps, churn spinning wheels and other stuff on tables on

the veranda. He still went to auction sales during the week, but on Friday, Saturday, and Sunday he stayed home and the big cars, such as Gray Dorts, Essex, Hupmobiles, and so on, with city licenses, started to call. His grounds looked like a garden party. Some went to Ab Walker, but most of them liked to do business with Joe.

That's when the women of the community really became interested in Joe. Local girls who normally wouldn't be caught dead around the so-called old stuff were haunting Joe Broome's. Mother said it was foolish for people who had lived all their lives among antiques to go looking for more of it. Father said they were after Joe as a husband.

A bunty-looking widow with a boyish bob appeared from Detroit. Morning, noon and night she hung around the "Anteeks." The women said it was a shame for a local man to marry a fortune hunter from the Michigan States. She was abusively fast and would use Joe for his money.

Joe fooled them. He sold the place to the widow and took a trip to Manitoba to see a cousin who had never returned from a harvest excursion. The widow was furious when she had to pay the full amount of the sale agreement to Mr. Henderson at the bank, saying in a moment of rash confidence to the banker she had expected Joe to propose.

She was game, however, because she repainted the place, sorted the stock into neat sections and put a properly spelled sign for "Antiques." She went out of business in six months and went back to Detroit, after selling the house to a lightning-rod salesman.

Joe returned and took a permanent room in the Commercial Hotel, bought a radio, subscribed to two city newspapers, had the barber shave him every day, lived by lending money to farmers, and wore boughten suits from Jimmy Medd.

"What was your secret, Joe?" my grandfather asked him

one day. "You made a neat pile out of that old stuff, and yet that smart widow went bust."

"Trouble with her," observed Joe, as he knocked the ash from a five-cent cigar and smoothed down his vest, "was she knew how to spell, and nobody knew I could."

CHAPTER 22

HEAT AND FLIES

There came a time in every summer when the heat descended like a bond that sealed our valley. The sun came up blazing over the hills and poured its rays down without relenting so that, by noon, the combination of the stilled air and the sunshine seemed to hold everything in a firm grip.

When you walked, it was as if you were enclosed in a sheath of invisible fire and the stones and even the grass burned at the toughened soles of your bare feet.

The family rejoiced because this was haying and ripening weather, providing nature had supplied you with June and early July showers.

Fence corners that sheltered a normal group of weeds became miniature jungles, and you could find relief by crawling under a monster burdock plant where the earth was shaded and still cool.

For the first two days you had the blessed relief of night when timid breezes came up the valley from the river and the swale and poked in at the curtains and soothed you on your bed.

But the heat went on and the house dried and warmed and became hot so, even at night, the earth and buildings that had been bombarded by the sun all day seemed to hold the heat and leave you breathless and gasping. The night breeze had a breath and there was a dry and metallic rustle to the leaves.

The cicada shrilled and sheets were hot and the pillow couldn't be cooled by simply turning it over. Escaped feathers from the tick had a habit of gluing themselves to your sweating body. Bedsprings creaked, betraying the light and restless sleep of tired people.

If you stood by the window you could hear the murmuring movement of the stock or the protesting screech of wire through a staple as an itchy beast rubbed against it.

Sometime, and you never could remember when, you drifted off to sleep—when you came awake the world was standing in the full glare of the sun again.

There was no early morning respite because the heat just seemed to intensify.

In the garden or amongst the lawn flowers your mother would be moving with her charges against another assault by the sun. She would stop to examine a forming cucumber or a tomato, cut lettuce to be brought in and kept dampened for dinnertime.

A robin with an inquisitive cock to her head followed Mother, looking at the dampened spots for worms to feed the fat youngsters who teetered along behind her. It was amusing to notice that they were already bigger than their mother and still depending on her for food.

On such hot days there was a fascination in being asked to go out to the old stone milk house and get milk, cream, butter, and eggs. Behind the stout walls there was still a cool dampness. The hard-packed dirt floor felt like balm on your feet. The walls were damp and cool to your hand.

There was always something to nibble—a cold potato or

some leftover meat from supper. Add a green onion from the garden and you had a stolen feast.

The guardian hens kept up a noisy vigilance over their respective broods in the orchard. When you looked up to the sky you found the reason. There was a fascination that approached the hypnotic in the sight of a hawk that glided slowly and seemingly without motion on mysterious air currents.

While the world was in the grip of the heat there was an undercurrent of savagery, which you noticed when you saw the barn cats stalking the young robins, trying to get them away from the vigilance and wisdom of the mother.

Day by day as the heat continued and the work progressed there was a subtle change in the surroundings. The grass bleached to a yellowish brown and the stock moved from the dry hillsides to the gully bottoms. There was color, too, as the green stalks of corn shot higher and higher. The orange lilies looked like tongues of flame in the border punctuated by blue spikes of delphiniums. The wild roses seemed to wither, but the petunias, nasturtiums, and pansies responded, as if by magic, to your mother's dipper and pail in the early evening.

The water level shrank in the pond, leaving a silver-green scum along the edges. The black water of the creek grew sluggish, and snakes sunned themselves on sandy banks. There was talk that if the water went any lower the gristmill might have to close down. Farmers anxiously checked their wells.

In the hot and lifeless days the windmills looked dejected, responding only feebly to an occasional wisp of breeze, while farmers complainingly pumped by hand.

Nature was a tease, however. Thunderheads would roll up over the distant hills like a war party, and, after hovering for a time, they vanished. Sometimes when the sky dark-

ened the breezes would stir the idle windmills and men in
the fields hurried to finish a field or a swath. The air would
cool with a sweet breath and then gradually the heat came
back and the sun looked as if it were laughing at the joke.

"Well," the men would say, wiping their brows or pausing to drink from a pail of water, "they must have had rain
across the river."

It wasn't jealousy, and there was hope as they added,
"This hot spell can't keep on much longer."

There were annoyances as well. Tempers frazzled and
sparked like flint. Cattle would find a weak spot in a fence
and surge in to gorge on green hay or corn. A nosy cow
would make a raid on the garden. A beast anxious for green
feed might eat something and gorge on water and mysteriously bloat, so work had to be suspended while the veterinarian was called.

Cows were hard to find for milking because they sought
refuge in the drying swale from heat and the tickling devil-
ishness of warble flies.

On a hot day like this the village was almost lifeless. The
hounds dozed in the shadow of the veterinarian's office;
the houses looked silent with drawn, green blinds; retired
couples sat on verandas, their rockers barely moving. The
only sign of full motion was the elaborate bamboo fans
operated by a foot treadle on the Tilly sisters' side veranda.
Most people considered this to be an affectation, depending on a rolled newspaper for breath relief.

I was never quite certain why we went to the village on
such a hot day, but welcomed the fact we made trips into
almost all the places. Standing under the green, striped
awning of the barbershop you smelled the heady lotions
and heard the steady talk of the barber coming in rhythm
with the snip-snip of his shears. It was punctuated by an
occasional grunt of assent or dissent from a chair customer.

It was dim and dark behind the screen door of the back room of the Commercial Hotel. Low voices murmured, rising and falling as if even passions were subdued by heat, and you sniffed yeasty aroma. Somehow it betrayed a lack of faith in the rigid intent of the Canada Temperance Act. Ours was supposed to be a "dry" county. Father handed me a five- or ten-cent piece, depending on his mood, and self-consciously urged me in the direction of Lee's Café.

"Better get yourself something to cool off with," he muttered, one hand on the wire catch of the door, "gotta see a man in here . . ."

His words trailed off as he vanished into the mysterious darkness, and I never did know the purpose of his call. It didn't bother me, because in those days, the main street of our village spelled adventure. It was only an irregular trailing of houses, false-front stores, and several churches that fronted for the houses scrambling behind it into some form of street patterns. It twisted by the elm tree with the big, protruding branch that sheltered the long, low building known as Olsen's Blacksmith.

Inside the café the hot air was moving sluggishly with the prompting of a two-bladed fan suspended from the ceiling. It looked like a barely turning propeller. At this time of day it was usually deserted. The "bratt" of the electric bell would bring smiling Jimmy Lee from the swinging door of the kitchen, his feet slapping flatly in their sandals on the oiled floor.

I always hoped that he might be busy or late in coming out. There was a fascination in just staring at the rows of pop bottles that served as advertisements and also to hold up a glass shelf for a display of pies and cakes and cookies, covered with cheesecloth against the raiding flies. There was also the ritual of looking in the big glass case beside the tobacco and cigarette case, at the display of penny candies and chocolate bars.

Jimmy was a kind man. He always put on a fly raid when I was alone in the café. With whoops and agility of wrist and elbow he wielded his flyswatter while I pondered the decision. The big marshmallow bars looked to be good value, but I had bought them before and found they turned soft and squishy with the heat, and it was hard to get them off without a great deal of undignified licking of the wrapper.

"Bottle of cream soda and two of those."

These were the halcyon days of two-for-five chocolate bars. They were made of a kind of indestructible, hard toffee that yielded a chocolate cover to the tongue but could be maintained soft but still manageable for later chewing.

Then I wandered down the street, finding shade on the front veranda of the general store. Sipping on the cream soda and nibbling on the leathery toffee center of one of the bars, I passed the time easily, only an occasional resident making a trip to the post office, or the drayman's horse moving along, disturbing the hot peace and quiet. Father would appear, whistling, make a purchase or two at the store, and we would start back slowly.

Father talked more than usual on the return trip, but I can't remember much of what he said, except for the usual statement when we reached the front gate.

"Humm . . . wouldn't say anything about the Commercial," he would suggest, and then, squinting at the heat rings around the sun, would add, "I think we're in for another scorcher tomorrow."

At night we sat as long as possible on the back stoop before going into the imprisoning heat of the house. The hired man spread blankets on the front veranda or even the grass, risking the insects in preference to the heat.

The grain flushed to yellowness and the cucumber blossoms shaped into cucumbers and the tomatoes started to redden and there was an unspoken anxiety about the place. Then, as hope was dwindling fast and pessimists hinted about army worms or grasshoppers, mother nature would grumble and thunder over the distant hills and the breeze would come surging up the valley and the sky would roll with clouds and the first splattering drops of rain would come to settle the dancing dust devils.

We didn't want to go into the house because it felt so good to stand and let the first drenching downpour cool the heat from your skin.

The hot spell was over and another cycle of nature had begun.

Then came the flies!

It was Mother who declared war on the flies. Flyswatters, made from squares of old screening, bound with rags and tacked to small handles were hung at convenient places throughout the house. Small sliding screens were placed in the upstairs windows. Fine mesh netting was tacked over the lower part of the downstairs windows. The cellar windows were inspected, and small pieces of screening salvaged from old screen doors were carefully worked to cover rusted and torn spots. Cheesecloth was tacked over the windows of the milk house.

Mother hated flies. They symbolized something unclean to her, and she waged a relentless war against them. With a reflex action she could be busy or talking and pick up a handy flyswatter, dispatch a fly, and replace the swatter, without a break in work or conversation. She was also frugal. When Father once brought home a rubber flyswatter she considered it to be an extravagance.

She bought other supplies in her campaign against the flies, however. Cheesecloth covered milk pans, food, and a variety of items.

She also had fly coils. They were those ingenious spools that unraveled and hung from the ceiling, exposing two sticky surfaces. In the kitchen they were out of your way but when she put them in the milk house or down in the cellar trouble frequently arose. On more than one occasion, while groping for apples or a jar of preserves in the dim cellar without bothering to light a lantern or a lamp, I came to grips with the tenacious stuff.

"There's nothing wrong with the fly coils," Mother reiterated, applying hot water and soap and cloth to the matted hair. "If you would just take time to do something properly and not try to avoid work by not taking a light."

Then, in our moment of despair she added insult to injury. "You've ruined a perfectly good fly coil. That's money wasted."

There was another weapon in the arsenal of fly attack that caused more than one disaster. This consisted of sheets of sticky flypaper. They came face to face and had to be separated before being spread out.

About eight by fourteen inches, they were a perfect size for trapping your feet when they blew from a table or were laid out on the floor of the front bedroom. More than once I have seen Grandfather coming out after getting his good suit coat for church, furiously flapping his foot trying to get the tanglefoot off the sole.

It caught flies. You could see them entangled in the brown, sticky material furiously trying to extricate themselves. It also caught elbows, papers, and almost anything that came within reach of it. On occasion the kittens became involved in it and I was certain once that Snap, our ancient collie, was going mad when he became stuck in two sheets of it that had been placed inside the back wood-shed door to trap the flies that crawled in through the crack under the door.

"I didn't think anybody used that door except myself," commented Mother, who then floored me by adding, "and may I also add that you were told expressly not to let that dog in the woodshed."

We also had fly pads. These were round, brown pancake affairs that were moistened and left on saucers as a kind of poison hemlock for thirsty and curious flies. After a few sips they turned up their heels and expired.

Some people were born fly catchers. Mrs. Henry Wilson was one. When she came to visit, she was always snapping out with her opened hand to nab flies and then cautiously peeking into the closed fist to examine the catch.

It was this propensity that almost broke up her husband's funeral. She was sitting in the second row of chairs, and the pallbearers were in the front row. Joe Alex Cargill, one of the pallbearers, was very bald, and a large blue fly kept circling the pink expanse like a plane about to land. Mrs. Wilson caught sight of it, and must have forgotten her grief for the thrill of the chase, although it was in the middle of the oration.

The fly circled closer and closer and people in adjoining pews, knowing her skill, started watching. The fly landed and her hand snaked out and grabbed. Unfortunately Joe Alex shifted and she bumped him hard on his bald spot. He reared up and looked back and hissed, "Liza, do you want me to go with your husband?"

It took Reverend McPherson some time to get back to the gist of his sermon, which fittingly enough concerned patience as an outstanding virtue of the late Henry Wilson.

CHAPTER 23
HARVEST GLORIES

Summer progressed slowly in the early part of July, with haying, but then it started to crowd in.

There came a day when a binder clickety-clacked on a hillside or in a valley, and the first wheat or the early oats were being cut. Even if your father complained that the neighbor was rushing the season, you felt the sign of the harvest on the land.

Road dust powdered the long grass and weeds by the side of the driveway and drifted across the front lawn. The young chickens looked strange with their partial feathering.

Every thunderhead and drifting cloud was examined carefully. A storm might flatten fields of grain. Cows were milked in the early morning and in the evening dusk, as the working day was stretched to the tiring point. A machinery break was a dreaded thing because it was a time-consumer.

The village of Clover was deserted, except for local residents, during the daytime. The stores stayed open at night for district farmers to do their shopping. Binder twine was piled high in front of the hardware store. There was a thriving business in machine oil and axle grease.

It was a time when city visitors strained the hospitality. A distant cousin and his brood always seemed to appear just about the time when work was at a peak. Father would make a dutiful visit to the house, look uncomfortable, and finally say, "Well, folks, I have to be getting back to work. One thing you can't hang onto in the country is fine weather."

Green apples produced uncomfortable results almost every year. On the other hand there was absolutely nothing to compare to the taste of the first Astrachans when they colored and reached the point of dark seeds. There was also a pilgrimage to be made to the grass farm for some delicious, small, wild apples that had a tang of their own. We also managed to make several trips to the wild raspberry patch that grew in profusion on slashes where bush had been removed.

Hard work and all, the country rang with some good times. There were garden parties and dances. Older people complained that they didn't know how young people could go to dances and do their work, comfortably forgetting earlier boasts about their own prowess of getting along so well on so little sleep in the busy season.

There was excitement! At least one barn in the district used to be sacrificed to fire each year. Experience never seemed to teach some people of the folly of storing green hay or wet sheaves.

If spontaneous combustion didn't do it, there was lightning.

A man who felt he couldn't afford lightning rods could be the poorer for economy.

There was tragedy too.

A man might be killed with a runaway team. Others were maimed by machinery, because this was the time when the country was moving over to mechanization and many men without mechanical skill or experience were making their initial contact with the danger and complication of the new equipment.

The ponds dried up, and the swale grew into itself, with the outer edges becoming firm underfoot.

Every year there would be a pall of smoke from burning roots in the peaty underground surface of the Long Swamp. By day it hung heavy over the swamp. Sometimes at night if you drove through it you would see a dull, reddish glow, and men would be called out to curb it from breaking into a fire that might threaten the timber.

Village boys used to pedal by on their bicycles, looking for fruit trees to rob. Their idleness seemed to be almost sinful in the face of so much activity in the country.

College students, especially in the depression, walked down country roads willing to trade subscriptions to magazines for a minimum of cash and something to eat.

Days merged into nights and nights into days in an almost hypnotic way. A boy didn't look at a calendar, as if the time might stretch magically if you didn't consult the figures.

Buyers started coming around looking for fat steers that had flourished on June grass. Stacks like weird thatched houses denoted bumper hay crops overflowing the barns.

Mother kept on suggesting the garden needed scuffling. Finally Father agreed, doing the root crops at the same time.

It was a miserably hot job, and a boy was appreciated if he took time to bring a honey pail filled with the crystal-clear water of the spring. The spring was a summer mystery; it kept a chill and seemed even colder because of summer heat.

Grandfather, urged to take it easy, one day would become aggravated enough by the sight of burdocks, milk weed, blue devil, and other gaunt weeds in the fence bottom and set out on a mission with his scythe. With a burdock leaf under his hat, he left the interlopers to die and wither.

Later in the evening he sat on the back stoop, a man satisfied with a job well done, and, smoking on his old pipe, recounted stories of cradling grain and then flailing it when he was a small boy.

He remembered the small separator driven by horse power, and you detected a note of wistfulness for "those days."

I really felt summer going from me when the old threshing machine came thumping up the road and a neighbor threshed his wheat in the field.

The threshermen were a noble and admired breed of men in the days of my country memory.

Where the role of being a railroad engineer was beyond our reasonable hopes, there was a true possibility that a boy on the farm could grow up and become a tank man or a separator man. The acme of the hope was to be the engine driver.

That was really a job for a man!

The steam engine was a snorting monster with an amazing capacity for consumption of rails or buzz wood. It provided its own mobility, hauling the separator from farm to farm. In movement it was lumbering with a majesty of its own, in spite of the jerky movements caused by the two iron wheels up front negotiating the rough road.

I suspect that the threshing gang knew they were heroes in a way to children in the country. Up the side road the outfit came, with the engine skittering a bit on the road and the separator rattling as if it was going to shake apart.

The tank man stopped by the creek to fill the tank wagon, and while the engine whistle gave two shorts and a long, which signaled it was coming to our place.

Father fussed around the barn, and Grandfather piled up bin boards in the granary. Mother had the table set, no matter what time of day the threshers came. Several of the neighbor girls came to fuss and "help," although the real work was all done in the way of cooking.

It was a prerogative to race down the road and look anxiously at the engine man, who might give an encouraging nod, and you slipped up and got caught and put up on the big box at the side or on a fender and told, "Hang on, boy, for dear life." It was a jolting, bone-jarring thrill of a lifetime.

"Like to give a pull on the whistle?"

A real hero of an engineer let you do that just as you came abreast of the back kitchen. Mother would come scurrying to the screen door and hold up her hands in horror, but you were safe. No one questioned the engine man.

There was the ritual of setting up for threshing. The separator had to be negotiated onto the barn floor. The separator man went about his business of getting the machine ready and the engineer moved the engine into place.

The big belt was slapped over the flywheel. There was a certain amount of bracing and placing, and the table was set up for the separator. The men of the "bee," who had assembled from neighboring farms and waited on the grassy slope beside the gangway, moved into place. The separator man waved to the engineer. The machine "chuffered" into action with the grabby fingers of the feeder snatching at the first experimental sheaves.

Then, all of a sudden, the threshing was on. The sheaves were pitched from man to man, to the "spike" man, who disposed of them in such a way as not to cause a choke-up.

The first spurts of grain came "whusting" down the spout and into the bushel boxes or the bin, depending on how it was being handled. The straw spurted in bursts, and then settled into a steady, golden stream. The dust rose like a veil of light, amber fog in the barn, and you couldn't see the separator man as he vanished beside the machine. The figures in the mows were dim.

When the tank man filled the small portable tank and started back to refill the main tank, it was a signal to go with him.

Tank men were casual fellows who never seemed to be in a hurry. They expended a slow and deliberate amount of energy in pushing the handle of the old, one-lunger pump and plenty of time recounting fanciful stories for our edification.

They hinted about love affairs with an amazing variety of community belles and asked pointed questions about the girls who would be waiting on table at dinnertime.

When I think of threshing, I remember a lot of separate things. There was the veeing sway to the belt and the uneven sound of the engine and the chattering roll of the separator.

There was the way the grain spilled in spurts from the spout, depending on the feeding. There were times when the separator man was furious because he felt the sheaves had been deliberately thrown in to choke up the feeder box when the men in the mow were getting too much dust or barley awns or thistles.

I can still hear the sound of a stone clattering around inside the machine and the way the separator signaled to cut off the power or flipped the belt off before some harm could come to the innards of his separator.

An outside stack was a glory to behold as it was shaped by a man with the spout of the blower.

Men took pride in being good stack men.

The sunlight filtered in between the barn boards and carved golden slices in the dust. The barn cats, wary of the noise and excitement, patrolled on the floor, looking for mice flushed from the mows. Pigeons disturbed from their normal roosting places, fluttered on the barn roof or around the driving shed.

At threshing time, Mother did all her cooking on the range in the summer kitchen. For some reason or other, the big kitchen always seemed to be cool for the threshing meal. The blinds were kept drawn, but the wind cross-ventilated the place when they were raised at noon.

The table had extra leaves in it, and it was covered by tablecloths. I remember a city relative being shocked at seeing white tablecloths used for a meal where the threshers were going to sit down.

"White cloth for those dirty men?"

Mother put her in a special place. "They're guests!"

It was fortunate the threshing coincided with the time when the garden was in full bloom. The sight of plates of sliced tomatoes, green onions, radishes, crisp, fresh lettuce in bowls, boiled beets, small carrots swimming in butter, and new potatoes with wisps of delicate skin sticking to their boiled sides were enough to make anyone hungry.

Still, the backbone of the meal was roast beef and baked ham. The girls swooped around, making certain that there were full platters on the table at all times, and there was no talk.

The threshers ate with the same determination as they worked.

Then, on came the bowls of preserves and the pies. Pie was a staple, and a man was expected to sample each kind. It was a poor housewife who hadn't several varieties of pies on her table.

When the meal was over, the men went out to sprawl on the grass, and while the older men caught forty winks the younger joshed each other.

As if by a mysterious sense, the men went back to work. The separator man went first to tinker at his machine, the engine man to fire up, and the tank man ambled over to see if his team had been fed.

We watched a trifle sadly to see the threshing come to an end. Finally it was over. The engine backed up and hauled the separator away, followed by the tank. As the outfit turned out the gate and went away up the road, the men scattered for home.

Father swept the barn floor and Grandfather tucked up odds and ends. As a boy, I felt the regret that all must feel when an eagerly anticipated event has finished.

On Fridays in both Catholic and Methodist homes plates of fried eggs and in some cases canned salmon would appear out of deference to the "fish eaters." Housewives complained that the Protestants were inclined to regard this as a treat and shun the meat.

Black Jack Cassidy was known as a stingy man with food. Generous to a fault when it came time to stand treat at the Commercial Hotel, he was niggardly about food. In a day and age of exchanging works, and when Catholics and Protestants alike were proud of good tables for such trading, they shunned working with Black Jack. The result was that he had to hire a crew headed by Ed Black. Ed was a religious man, and a lay reader at the red-brick Methodist church in Clover.

He laid down an ultimatum to Cassidy. No meat, Friday or any day, no work. Cassidy agreed, and rumor spread that an elderly sheep had vanished from his flock just before threshing. Some said it was old age that had removed the beast, but when the men went into the Cassidy kitchen to the pervading smell of mutton, they knew the answer.

Black Jack graciously suggested Ed say grace. Ed lowered his head and recited an impromptu grace that still delights residents of our community:

"*O Lord of Love,*
Look down from above,
On us poor sinners below,
And give us meat that we can eat,
And take away this tough, old ewe."

CHAPTER 24
SUMMER INTO AUTUMN

We savored the last days of August and Labor Day in much the same way a condemned man must feel during his last few days in Death Row. Uncle Jim used to say being in love was like having a pain inside you couldn't itch. The days before school started brought a similar kind of pain.

We walked into the orchard and even sun-warmed apples that were winy and juicy couldn't tempt a bite. Kittens frolicking in the tall grass or the whimsicality of a buffoon rooster failed to bring respite from the heart numbness. In two days or three days it seemed as if all this would be over. Frantically you tried to remember where the days had vanished.

Memories were like rosary beads. There was the strawberry social, the time you went to the city when your mother had to see the eye specialist, the trip to the lake on the Fourth of July, three days visiting a cousin, the church garden party, several days when you helped in your uncle's general store.

There was work in connection with summer holidays. Picking berries wasn't such a bad job. Hoeing turnips and mangels on the other hand could bring a shiver of unpleasant memory. Like someone reaching for a sweet after a sour taste, you could remember the time the ice cream freezer salesman had given the demonstration at Henderson's.

I used to hate the weekend before Labor Day. I even had tricks about it. One was to try and stay up later, as if by doing so there could be a slowing down of the passing hours. It didn't work. In fact, my parents used to let me sleep later in those few days and it seemed as if that made the days shorter.

Labor Day wasn't anything but another day of hard work on the farm. Mother was particularly busy with pickling and preserving and the kitchen had that special, spicy smell about it that could make your nose tingle and your mouth water.

"Mother, when, for instance, do you think I can quit school?"

She usually didn't hear the question the first time but when it was repeated she would stand and look at me with a half smile.

"If children like you could only have a better taste of what life is all about, when you get older, you'd never complain about school."

Then she was off to sterilize more sealers or swish the soaking pickles, spices, and vinegar in a crock that were waiting to be transferred to sealers. She always left me a little confused and somehow suspicious of the conspiracy of grownups in promoting school attendance for youngsters and never for themselves.

In the still darkness of the bedroom, the night of Labor Day was a strange experience. Some things started to pop into your mind about going back to school. New books and a new teacher always brought a faint flicker of interest. There was a new family in the township.

Suddenly in the half light of very early morning, you found the desire to go to school. There was interest and curiosity and I guess a certain amount of resignation. After all it was inevitable. Even Joe Kelly, who used to hide out in the woods for the first two or three days of each school term, was finally apprehended and brought to school.

Groping at the washstand that served as a bureau, dresser, and desk you found a bundle of clothes. Sometime during the night your old clothes had been removed and new ones put in their place. They were new to you, but seldom "store bought new!" They were most likely to be cut down from hand-me-downs.

"Feels good to be going back to school," observed Father, year after year. "Wish I were going."

You didn't have the nerve to tell him you wished he were going in place of you.

Grandfather, a sprightly but elderly widower, could always manage to shock Mother.

"Saw the new teacher. Sprightly thing too. Might take a wander over and have a chat with her. Looks as if she would be the marryin' kind."

Mother invariably bit and then, flustered, sent us packing to school. Stones didn't bother summer toughened feet. We dawdled by the creek bridge, tasted the wild apples on the Leslie place, teased the Macfarlane bull, heaved a few stones at telephone insulators, and finally arrived at the schoolhouse.

There was a bit of awkwardness in the schoolroom. The smaller children cried, a few mothers lingered for a time, the varnish smelled strange, and it was a bit sticky on the seats. The older boys took advantage of the new teacher to form a sort of wolf pack around the stove, anticipating the opportunity of gossip and winter comfort. It would only take a few days for her to settle that clique.

The place soon had a smell of chalk in it. There was a certain fascination in heading up new scribblers, spluttering with new pen nibs and looking at the pictures in the new books. By the time you were nine or ten, however, school wasn't such a bad place. You had enough seniority to at least get a few turns at bat during the noon hour ball game.

But autumn came, and the remembered autumns of childhood stand out like a series of highly colored vignettes with depth and perspective beyond that of any paintings. An artist to capture the memories of a child in the country in the peaceful days between Great War and Great Depression would have to use many skills. Painting and etching would be only part of the whole. Somehow there would have to be room for the senses of smell and hearing.

There was first of all the obvious enjoyment of my grandfather in absorbing the fullness of the sun while sitting in the lee of the woodshed, woodpile, or back kitchen. With a battered knife whose blade had been sharpened to a stiletto-like shape he would peel off the rosy skin of a McIntosh or the tawny, tough hide of a russet apple. He prided himself on being able to bring it off in a spiraling string without breaking it. Then he would hold it up, without saying anything, because his artistry spoke for itself. Casually the peeling would be flung aside to nervously contract back to shape. It seemed to be looking for the stolen middle or sometimes trying to protect the fleshy underside from the buzzing flies.

Autumn had lazy, fog shrouds caused by warm days and chilly nights. They were like the dressing for a fantasy, parting at the gesture of the sun but staying on in the protected, low, marshy spots sometimes until almost noon. Stable windows misted and the iron pump handle sweated. The grass was awash. Silvered rails looked slimy while cold-stiffened flowers seemed unreal and artificial.

I liked the season when her trick was to gently unfold the display of colors, in place of the sudden night raid of frost which transformed the world in a nocturnal change of scenery. It was more fun when a few trees assumed bright crimson or red and stood in contrast to the remaining green ones. A pasture maple would blaze out after a night of abandonment, but grass and laneway trees stood fast. In the midst of evergreens a tree might stand out in gold and red like a sentinel. The frost demons touched only certain ones, building up a grand finale, whetting the senses for each unfolding day.

In tune with the extravaganza a purplish haze crept into our days, after the sparkling vitality of early September. The blue and green waters turned khaki dark. Foam-flecked and carrying the first colored leaves like jeweled galleons, the creek and river mysteriously covered the mysteries of the graveled bottom as if protecting its winter-expectant life from prying eyes. The splashing, gurgling sounds of spring and summer waters changed to a deeper and solemn tone. It was as if the spirit of the waters was preparing for the time when an icy grip would deprive it of freedom and hold it in solid winter bondage.

Birds always seemed busy in the middle time of autumn. The chattering starlings blackened the stubble fields and then at the edge of night and the break of day they gabbled in the trees. They had a nervous intent in gobbling up as much as possible, almost as if winter would mean hibernation. Because we were on the flyway we watched each day for southward bound geese and ducks. Perhaps we didn't really want to see them. There was something final in the sight of the V-shaped flocks that left a touch of sadness. It gave a landlocked country boy a bittersweet vision. Somewhere in that south toward which they headed the sun would glint on blue water and white sandy beaches at the edge of the impenetrable jungles he had read about, but had little hope of ever seeing.

On the hilly slopes of the valley walls which hemmed us in under the spread of autumnal sky populated by special cloud clusters I used to wander. There were many walls of stone on the slopes. They were remnants of old houses and barns of an earlier generation. They stayed as monuments to people and to the destruction of fire and the erosion of time. These were fieldstones picked at random and set in place by hands as roughened by labor as the stones were by the ministrations of wind, sun, rain, and time. These old walls glowed with color and glinting crystals of what we fondly believed to be precious stones.

Here were the vines and creepers of scarlet and crimson. You could also find poison ivy deceptively glossy in a burnished and faded yellow or a startling orange. Once to every boy there came a painful experience. Mine came in a twofold way. I picked the autumn-tinted vine to appease a teacher for a bout of homework undone. She innocently took them and displayed them in a vase.

"Look at the pretty flowers."

There was an ominous chuckle from bigger boys.

"That will be enough out of you two," she glared stamping a dainty foot, "I think it was thoughtful of Harry to bring these bright leaves as a sample of what nature gives us as a reward each autumn."

She fluffed them out a bit and looked around the room.

"Now as a nature lesson I want you to identify these leaves."

Big boy snapped his fingers.

"Yes," she said coldly.

"It's poison ivy," blurted the boy.

"It's not," she replied, "it's Virginia creeper."

"Haw, haw," replied the boy, "you'll find out."

He was made to stand in the corner. Teacher and pupil,

in this case myself, two days later shared a common experience. We broke out in blisters.

Autumn was a time of contrasts. The corn stood like wigwams in rows of shocks. Stocks of ripening hayseed were blackened. The fields of fall seeding sprouted a new green like a springtime renewed. Fat pumpkins sprawled out in diminishing vines. The grapes along the fence rails looked appetizing, but after the experience of the poison ivy I could never muster up enough courage to try them.

CHAPTER 25

THE MEANING OF THE WORD

With the coming of the new school year our mothers were greatly relieved. They were of the opinion two months was enough to reduce the average boy to a state of heathenism. Thus we moved back into stricter physical discipline but also closer to the religious core of our existence. We moved nearer to the Word, and Word was Love.

It was used a lot. Fights, tantrums, swearing, temptation, and it seemed as if everything transgressed against the fundamental rule of loving God and your neighbor. We were fairly certain it was sometimes badly abused as far as grownups were concerned, but didn't have any of the logic necessary to reason against the dictums.

There was also the discipline. At the separate school we opened with prayers, were reminded about our duties toward morning and evening prayers and Grace before and after meals. At noon there was the Angelus, something we didn't have to be reminded about, because the teacher had a rather complicated honor system for selecting boys to go and pull the bell ropes at St. Peter's to toll the noonday Angelus.

I could remember it vividly because during my first attempt there was the embarrassment of having the bell flip over, taking the rope with it several times and leaving me dangling from the floor. On the return trip around it dumped me unceremoniously while causing a panic in the township, because the bell was tolled in a rather unorthodox manner as a fire alarm.

The Word of God was intermingled in our lives. Much of it, by way of catechism, was learned by memorizing, and while much significance escaped, there was still a powerful residue. We were, for instance, filled with the awe-inspiring consequences of sin. Every one of the grownups, it seemed, took turns in giving us a healthy respect for having anything to do with the devil or his works. Visiting missionaries at the Catholic church rivaled the revivalists at the Protestant churches in describing Eternity.

"If," intoned a very large priest, at a mission, in a voice that dwindled to a powerful whisper, "you took away one grain of sand per year from all the seashores of North America until you had taken them all away . . . remember this . . ."

Then he paused and raised his voice until the stained-glass windows rattled, "Remember this, when you had exhausted every seashore on this whole, vast continent then Eternity would hardly have begun . . ."

I spent several frustrating hours afterward in trying to count the grains of sand in the pile in the backyard left over after plastering the kitchen ceiling, but had to give up.

It made me dizzy, however, to realize the consequences of sin, and I went around for at least a week in a numbed terror. Childhood resilience led me to recover, and the cherished knowledge that my grandfather felt people had to have a pinch of sin in their make-up to qualify as normal human beings.

There were other memories. There were times when the Living Presence seemed most real. It came for instance in the semi-darkened church on a blustery Lenten Friday afternoon during the recitation of the Way of the Cross. It seemed exuberant and happy on an Easter Sunday. It touched with a sharp itch on Good Friday when it was easy to imagine the happenings at Golgotha. At other times, under the influence of teacher or mother or priest, the blue sky was heaven almost touching the earth. It was a comfort to be able to look at the heavens and know that the evil of hell was locked away out of sight at least.

Henry Higgins was my playmate, and it was natural, in spite of the careful precaution of not discussing it that we took from the example of our parents, that we sometimes moved under emotion to talk about religion. I knew that the white-brick Methodists had a plainer service than we did, without the colorful vestments, incense candles, and ritual. At the same time I envied Henry for one thing, and so we used to meet clandestinely back at the sugar shanty and sing hymns.

Henry had it over me when it came to hymns, and so the meandering Maitland River became the Jordan as we tried to bellow out in ragged unison such hymns as "Shall We Gather at the River" and "We'll Cross the River Jordan." I especially enjoyed "Throw Out the Lifeline."

Since our friendship was a deep one, we did wonder sometimes about having to go to different schools. Questioning our parents about religion brought as evasive answers as when the matter of sex came up. In a sense we tried to find the similarities between the religions and could only come to the conclusion that fear of sin and Love of God and Neighbor were about the only things we had in common.

I must have been searching for a sign of some kind, and strangely enough it came the first time I ever saw a Negro. I was seven going on eight years of age. It was at the County Fall Fair . . . I suppose I would have been a lot more excited if there hadn't been a midway. In fact, the Negro was with the midway, so it just seemed natural to see him.

"Hello there, boy."

It was his voice I remembered. It made me vibrate because it was deep and low and rumbling like a pipe organ. I had been staring in through the snow fence at the mysteries of the merry-go-round when I heard the voice and jumped back.

"Don't be frightened, boy. It won't hurt you."

It wasn't much of a midway, but it looked wonderful to my eyes. There were several games of chance and a fish-pond, a rather bedraggled-looking gypsy who told fortunes, a tottering ferris wheel, and the merry-go-round.

Flashes of former glory remained in glints of red, green, and gold paint and a few banners that fluttered from the pinnacle of the tent-shaped merry-go-round. Somewhat battered-looking figures of animals pumped up and down as they rotated around the center where there was a grunting little engine.

"You ever ride one of these contraptions?" asked the big man.

"No."

"You like to?"

"Sure would."

The rich laughter poured out like fresh taffy.

"Well, boy, when you come back to the fair you look for me . . . Archie, and I'll see you get a ride."

My father called me then. I had a half-notion to ask if I could stay until the family came to the fair, but it was a hopeless idea so I went home and lived with a bursting excitement until it was time to get back.

There's something about the music of a calliope that has a siren call to it. Perhaps that's because it seems related to the sound of a steam train. Few people can resist that sound, and although this midway was a tiny affair and the merry-go-round was a relic, the crowd around it was enormous.

My parents had ideas that were contrary to mine. They wanted me to spend the afternoon with either one of them, and I wanted freedom. For one thing I wanted to get back and visit my new friend, Archie, and there was a lingering suspicion in my mind of what their reaction might be. I tried slipping away in a dense crowd in front of the exhibit building but I was caught and finally on the verge of tears I was allowed to go in company with my grandfather.

"Gramp, do you know any black men?"

My grandfather was used to my questions, but this one stopped him in his tracks.

"Well, oh . . . let me see . . . used to be a swamper in the lumber woods called Charlie . . . and I remember a cook, too, one year . . . why?"

I urged him on through the crowd as I explained. I had been promised a ride on the merry-go-round by Archie.

"Hold on there," laughed my grandfather, "I've got money. You don't have to ride for nothing."

Then he stopped and scratched his head. That's what I always liked about my grandfather. He understood right away that there was something special about getting a ride on a merry-go-round when you were the guest of a black man called Archie, who liked you well enough at first sight to make the promise.

Archie, wearing a black silk hat and a frock coat over a collarless shirt, was in charge of the merry-go-round. He operated a lever that started and stopped it, watched to see that everyone was safely hanging on and ushered the patrons off after a ride. A fat, painted-looking woman was taking money in a little booth.

I tried to get Archie's eye. Just then something happened. The crowd had come off the merry-go-round and more were waiting behind the little gate in the snow-fence barricade to get on. Mrs. Ben Tidell was yelling about being robbed.

"I had two ten-dollar bills in my wallet and that man must have taken them when he helped me off."

She was pointing at Archie. I knew, with all the desperate loyalty of a child, that it couldn't be this man, but Grandfather held me with a grip of iron. I could sense something in the crowd, and although it was hard to keep watching, because I was short, and the crowd swept over me, I noticed an angry, muttering sound.

"Search him."

"Bloody thief."

Archie's face seemed to turn blue-gray. Bert Timms, the township constable, came up, and there was a lot of argument. Mrs. Tidell was half crying and screaming.

She was convinced that Archie was the thief and demanded that he be taken off to jail.

Just then her daughter Margaret came up, and I saw her put her arm around her mother's shoulders. Mrs. Tidell blushed and crouched against the booth and through the legs of the crowd I could see her raise her skirt and take something from a petticoat. It was the money she had pinned there and forgotten.

Even at seven I could see and feel the sense of futile regret that passed through the crowd. They melted away from the merry-go-round, and Mrs. Tidell was crying and I saw Archie leaning against the figure of a horse.

Everybody hung back, and the merry-go-round looked pathetic and deserted. Then something happened. The hangers-on gasped when Father Morrison and Reverend McPherson walked up to the ticket booth, bought tickets, and handed them to Archie, who straightened up and gave them a respectful, little bow.

"Come on," said my grandfather, "let's both ride the merry-go-round. It looks safe for both Methodists and Catholics." He bought the tickets and, walking in past the little barricade, handed them to Archie. Grandfather put out his hand and said, "Glad to meet you, Archie. My grandson says you're a friend of his."

The blue-gray face turned shining black, the teeth shone, and the velvet laughter poured out. "He sure is, sir. Don't forget you folks is havin' a extra ride on me."

"Be glad to," said Grandfather, reaching into his vest pocket. "Have a cigar, Archie."

Soon the merry-go-round was going, and the crowd was thicker than ever, and although nothing seemed changed, I knew it had.

I changed. I learned something about the Word of God and Love thy Neighbor and Love God and all that. I never had any hesitation afterward tipping my hat to either Reverend McPherson or Father Morrison and even found that I had no fear of them.

My only trouble came when I met Mrs. Tidell. Later on, I came to realize that was the continuing test for all Methodists or Catholics or, I suppose, for all religions. One thing I did know! What Mrs. Tidell did wasn't like the pinch of sin that Gramp had been talking about.

PaperJacks

MOSTLY IN CLOVER
by Harry J. Boyle

An open door to an era full of warm nostalgia, this is a collection of articles that Harry Boyle contributed to *The Telegram*, edited for book publication, and rescued for a wider immortality than the yellowed newsprint clippings pinned to kitchen walls in rural Ontario. *Harry Boyle* has "a marvellous power to evoke the sounds and sights and smells and feelings of a boyhood gone ... commands the eye and the heart of the reader in every page". – *Burton T. Richardson in the foreword.* $1.50

A SUMMER BURNING
by Harry J. Boyle

A Canadian farm boy learns the hard facts of life from a young hoodlum fresh out of the slums of Toronto in this piquant novel about a lad's two worlds.

At fifteen, Joey Doyle knew only the world that surrounded the Ontario farm on which he lived – a world of nature and simplicity. But in his sixteenth summer – when Sammy Adams, a tough city boy, came to live at the farm for a few months – Joey was suddenly exposed to a world he had never imagined, in which tobacco and liquor, sex and prostitution, crime ... and death, played principal roles. $1.50

PaperJacks

GENTLE PIONEERS
Five Nineteenth-Century Canadians
by Audrey Y. Morris

To the harsh pioneering land of Upper Canada in the 1830s came Susanna Moodie, John W. Dunbar Moodie, Catharine Parr Traill, Thomas Traill and Samuel Strickland. This brilliant biography of a family group shows these people not just as literary and historical personages, but as the individuals they were, with human weaknesses and frailties. It is a vivid portrait of a group who lived through appalling hardships to become noble and "gentle pioneers". $1.95

RAT RIVER TRAPPER
by Thomas P. Kelley

They called him "the mad trapper" and "the man who steals gold from men's teeth". But no one knows, to this day, who this strange loner, who wandered through the Yukon in the 1920s with a smoking rifle in his hands, really was. *Thomas P. Kelley*, author of the best-seller *The Black Donnellys*, attempts to unravel this mystery of the Canadian North. $1.50